THE

CANADA'S FIRST VICTORIA CROSS
Born in 1833 a short distance north of this site, Alexander Dunn was educated at Upper Canada College and at Harrow, England. In 1853 he was commissioned Lieutenant in the 11th Hussars. A participant in the charge of the Light Brigade at Balaclava on October 25, 1854, he saved the lives of two of his regiment by cutting down their Russian attackers, and thus became Canada's first winner of the newly-created Victoria Cross. In 1858 Dunn helped to raise the 100th Royal Canadian Regiment, which he later commanded. In 1864 he transferred to the 33rd (Duke of Wellington's) Regiment, and four years later was accidentally killed while hunting in Abyssinia.
Archaeological and Historic Sites Board of Ontario.

HISTORIC MARKER
IN TORONTO'S CLARENCE SQUARE

The story of Lieutenant Alexander Dunn, 11th Hussars, appears on page 4.

THE BRIDGE AT DIEPPE

and other Canadian war stories

by Mabel Tinkiss Good

illustrated by George Pepper

GRIFFIN HOUSE
Toronto 1973

ISNB 0 88760 061 1

Published by Griffin Press Limited
455 King Street West, Toronto M5V 1K7 Canada

PRINTED IN CANADA

Affectionately dedicated to

The Family,

and in tribute to
All Who Served
1939-1945

"To youth, the dying hands of heroes give
The world, to mould on patterns dimly dreamed
By those who died that clear-eyed youth might live.
And youth must take, with hearts that proudly know
The price their elder brothers paid in blood,
That liberty, and love, and hope might grow.
The story, written bravely without tears,
Yet oft in bitter anguish and despair,
Must fall like pibroch peals on youthful ears,
Lest they forget."

M.T.G.

PREFACE

If this small volume would carry faithfully to young people (and perhaps their elders) the message I have to send, its words must, of necessity, in the words of Rudyard Kipling "become alive and march up and down in the hearts of hearers". Since I cannot lay claim to such genius, I can only hope that some small flame from the fiery truth of the contents may warm, in passing, the souls of my readers.

It is hoped sincerely that readers will understand that, while individuals must necessarily be singled out in the following pages, thousands of others, no less brave, are thereby represented and honoured. It is indeed to be remembered that where one man is known and recorded in honour, many others, equally heroic, make up the glory that is Canada, the heritage that is Canadian, for Canadian generations to come.

These pages would seek to pay humble tribute to them all.

Many sources of reference have been carefully consulted and the facts checked as closely as is at present possible, seeking that truth. To the Departments of Public Relations, Intelligence and Information of the three fighting Services, I extend my appreciation.

I am most gratefully mindful of the encouragement, support and assistance afforded me by my family and friends; and, in particular to Mr. William Davidson, and Dr. G. F. G. Stanley, both lately of the Historical Section (Army), Department of National Defence; also to Dr. G. N. Tucker, Director of Naval Historical Section, Commander William Strange, R.C.N., and Lieutenant-Commander E. F. B. Watt, R.C.N.V.R. of his Staff; to Mr. W. H. Van Allen, Director of Publicity, Merchant Navy, Department of Transport, Captain H. Evans, Honours and Awards Section (Army), Department of National Defence; to Sergeant G. S. Howard, R.C.M.P., Editor *Royal Canadian Mounted Police Quarterly;* finally to Dr. Douglas Leechman and Mr. Charles Clay, Ottawa, for their friendly interest and counsel, and to Miss Olive Walker, Ottawa, for her faithful secretarial services.

M.T.G.

Arnprior, Ontario

PREFACE TO 2ND EDITION

Since publication in 1948 of the first edition of this book under title of "Men of Valour" many, if not most, of the events of the Second World War have come into focus in the perspective of thirty years. Fevered passions and panics have cooled and, to some degree, time has laid its healing touch on old and bitter hatreds and prejudices.

Judgments, always coloured by the shadow of tragedy and the confused paucity of fact at the time, take on the clarity of more considered truth. So it is with the fateful nine-hour battle at Dieppe, now forever a scarlet thread in the pattern of Canadian history.

Last year, on 19 August, 1972, Canada participated, at the invitation of the Mayor of Dieppe, and the French authorities, in ceremonies marking the 30th anniversary of the Dieppe raid. Attending were Canadian officials and dignitaries, regimental representatives, and surviving veterans of that other August day, and the two Dieppe Victoria Cross winners, John Foote and Colonel Cecil Merritt.

The occasion brought forth comments in which the Dieppe battle was referred to as 'the lost battle that won the war', and the conviction among those who know that without the bitter experience and knowledge gained by the Dieppe "rehearsal" the War might have come to a different end.

Canada's participation in the Dieppe raid was represented by The Queen's Own Cameron Highlanders of Ottawa, The Royal Regiment of Canada, The South Saskatchewan Regiment, The Royal Hamilton Light Infantry, The Essex Scottish, The Royal Canadian Engineers, The Calgary Tank Regiment, Les Fusiliers Mont-Royal and the Royal Marine "A" Commando, all supported by cover from the three arms of the service.

Colonel H. Des Rosiers, deputy Minister of National Defence, greeting seventeen Dieppe survivors who reached Canada in October, 1942, included in his welcome these words:

> "Canada has had many proud moments but few have been prouder than these .... these brave soldiers who inscribed upon the sands of Dieppe this nation's determination to fight for freedom's cause .... gave the oppressed peoples of the world a new measure of hope...."

In adding these words to those written in preface to the 1948 edition, I include grateful acknowledgement to many who have given their help and guidance in this present work.

Outstanding among these are Colonel G. Nicholson, S. F. Wise, Director, Directorate of History, Department of National Defence, and Phillip Chaplin, Assistant Director, Directorate of History, Department of National Defence, Mr. Fred Azar, Canadian War Museum, all of Ottawa, and Mr. Frank Lowe, Editor, Weekend Magazine, of Montreal.

My warm appreciation goes also to those who shared the work of preparing this manuscript for publication, Miss Ruby Tinkiss of Vernon, British Columbia, former Nursing Sister, who served with her unit in Scotland throughout the Second World War, and Mrs. Aileen Russell, of Montreal, Quebec, and—always to my family for unfailing encouragement.

M.T.G.
Montreal, Quebec.
May, 1973.

CONTENTS

CHAPTER		PAGE
	In Honour Remembered	1
One	The Bridge at Dieppe	12
Two	No Heroes, Please	21
Three	Grapnel Germany	29
Four	"Not on the Lone Prairie"	38
Five	Special Duty	44
Six	The Happy Warrior	50
Seven	Where Are Now Your Prophets?	57
Eight	It Was My Job	63
Nine	Just Luck	70
Ten	The True Glory	80
Eleven	Ils ne passeront pas.	91
Twelve	Padre X	99
Thirteen	Who Ride the Skies	107
Fourteen	A Christmas Present for "Mom"	114
Fifteen	Without Witnesses	121

ILLUSTRATIONS

Twirling his tin hat, he walked out onto the bridge, calling as he went, "See, there's no danger here!"

Yet grimly ... he gripped his wheel ... following every command.

In a flash, the Sergeant-Major ... tossed it back towards the enemy.

With infinite patience, he drew the thing into shallow water, foot by dangerous foot.

... he plunged forward, reaching out with both hands for the grenade.

... he lifted him in his strong arms, and carried him to whatever safety there might be.

Not fifteen yards from the gaping hole, the grim outline of a guard tower loomed darkly against the sky.

There the ship which had been torpedoed was standing on end, all ablaze.

... he dashed forward, pausing only to grasp a new weapon and a fresh supply of ammunition.

Paying no attention to the battle which raged about him, Captain Foote gave what simple aid he could ....

... the bombs fell whistling through the air. Straight to their target they went, with faultless aim.

When the tanks were almost on top of them, they suddenly opened fire.

In Honour Remembered

SINCE the romantic days of the noble King Arthur and his Round Table Knights, brave deeds have won special marks of honour. People all over the world thrill to the stories of those gallant men of long ago who rode abroad, seeking out wickedness to destroy it. When King Leodogran of the land of Cameliard was beset by "wild dog and wolf and boar" (in the words of Lord Tennyson) and assailed by enemies, he called upon King Arthur and his followers.

"Arise, and help us, thou! For here, between man and beast, we die," was the desperate cry. It did not go unheeded. Nor, indeed, was any call for help from the weak to the strong disregarded.

Stirring tales make mention of the different badges of honour worn by the brave and the strong during that valiant age. There was "the golden symbol of kinglihood", which was a dragon, signifying leadership, royal power, and authority. There was also the meaning associated with the peacock. This bird was served at table only on most momentous occasions, and he who was allowed to carve it was honoured in the highest degree. Indeed, the most solemn vows of the Knights were often made before roasted peacock. The idea seems to have been that the gorgeous bird in his pride was a fitting symbol of the honour to which an especially brave knight was entitled. It was said, too, that the eyes of the peacock signified the eyes of the world upon the hero and his heroism.

Another famous tradition of those early days was the nine jousts, or tournaments, held yearly by King Arthur. To the winner of each of these the King awarded a diamond from a royal crown. The tournaments were therefore called the "diamond jousts".

There have been many other symbols and badges of honour worn throughout the years. A Knight carried, emblazoned upon his shield, a record of his victories. Then, too, his fair lady often sent him forth to battle wearing a ribbon from her hair or frock. So heroes have ever justly won, by their gallant and unselfish deeds, proud recognition from ruling sovereigns and fellow-countrymen. Even so, today, we honour our heroes.

Each country has its own awards and decorations. The loftiest one in the British Empire is the Victoria Cross. Although there are many older honours to be won, this simple bronze Cross stands above all the others. It is named for the sovereign who instituted it—Victoria the Good. On 5 February, 1856, during the Crimean War, the War Office published the Royal Warrant for this award to be instituted, "to take precedence over all other Orders".

The opening words of the original proclamation read:

> "Whereas We, taking into Our Royal Consideration that there exists no means of adequately rewarding the individual gallant services . . . by these presents for Us, Our Heirs and Successors institute and create a new Naval and Military Decoration, which We are desirous should be highly praised and eagerly sought after . . ."

The award must be given only for a particularly brave act; and originally this had to be performed in the presence of the enemy. In 1858, however, it was ordained that deeds of great valour done *not* in the presence of the enemy might also be recognized by the honour. Nevertheless, only once, according to record, has there been an award under these circumstances. This was in 1867, when the Victoria Cross was bestowed upon Private Timothy O'Hea, of the 1st Battalion of the Rifle Brigade, for his outstanding bravery in helping to extinguish a fire in a railway car carrying ammunition. The courageous action took place in Canada during the Fenian Raid of 1866.

Anyone who twice qualifies for the Victoria Cross is entitled to have a bar attached to the ribbon, and an additional bar for every other time he may earn the honour; but available records appear to show that the Cross has never been won more than twice. It is conferred only after a recommendation has been carefully prepared by high-ranking officers, whose report must be supported by the signed statements of at least three witnesses to the brave act. Along with this recommendation is submitted the full story of the deed, which is called the citation. These documents are considered by the Victoria Cross Committee, which in turn passes them on to the reigning King or Queen for final approval. Notice of the award must then be published in the *London Gazette*, together with the official citation.

The winner of the Cross may receive it from the King (or Queen), or representative, in the presence of members of the Service to which he belongs. The presentation ceremony is called the Investiture.

The Cross itself is made of bronze taken from captured enemy guns when obtainable. It is 1½ inches across, with raised edges. On the front, called the obverse, is the British Lion standing on guard above the Royal Crown. Below the Crown, on a scroll, are the words, "For Valour". The back, called the reverse, carries the name and rank of the winner, and describes the act for which the Cross was granted, and where and on what date it took place. According to the original proclamation, the Cross must be worn on the left breast, hanging from a ribbon of blue for the Navy and of red for the Army. However, this was later changed to a claret-red ribbon for all Services. So it is today.

The man who receives the Victoria Cross is allowed to use the letters "V.C." after his name. He does not wear the Cross itself except on special full-dress occasions. At all other times, when in uniform, he wears only a ribbon with a tiny cross in the centre.

The very first Victoria Cross was won by Charles David Lucas during the Crimean War, on 21 June, 1854. For although the award was not instituted until two years later, it was made effective from the beginning of the war. The occasion arose during a heavy bombardment by the Russians. Lucas was serving on the British ship *Hecla*. A live enemy shell fell on the deck. Instantly, Lucas sprang forward, seized the shell, and threw it overboard, thus saving his ship.

The first to be won by a Canadian was also awarded during the Crimean War. The hero was Lieutenant Alexander Robert Dunn, serving with the 11th Hussars of the British Army at the famous Battle of Balaclava, 25 October, 1854. The first awarded to the Air Force was won by Second-Lieutenant W. B. Moorehouse of the British Royal Flying Corps at Courtrai, on 26 April, 1915. This gallant officer did not live to enjoy his honour. It was awarded after death (posthumously), however; for King Edward had added this ruling to the original warrant in 1902. Before this time, deeds of bravery performed at cost of the hero's life were announced officially, but no decoration was conferred. King Edward's amendment was made so that surviving relatives would receive the Cross on behalf of those who died after winning it, as far back as the Crimean War and the Indian Mutiny.

On 4 August, 1914, King George V ordained that posthumous awards might be publicly presented to the next-of-kin by His Majesty. This ruling does not permit next-of-kin, or any person other than the winner, to wear the Victoria Cross at any time. And any person who sells or gives away a decoration he has won is liable to severe punishment. If he loses it, however, he is permitted to obtain another at some slight cost. In like manner, a Victoria Cross winner who is convicted of treason, cowardice, or crime, will have his name erased from the Roll of Honour.

An impressive award of the prized recognition for gallantry was made in 1921, when the British Nation dedicated a Victoria Cross to honour the American dead in the Great War, 1914-1918. On 11 November, 1921, Armistice Day, by command of His Majesty George V, the decoration was laid by Admiral of the Fleet Earl Beatty of the North Sea on the tomb of the Unknown Warrior in the vault of the Memorial Amphitheatre at Arlington National Cemetery, Washington.

There have been approximately 1,300 Victoria Crosses won up to the present time. Of this number, 92 have been received by Canadians, and 34 of these were posthumously awarded. In World War II, 1939-1945, Canadians won 16 Victoria Crosses, 8 of them posthumously. Two of these went to the Naval Services, eleven to the Army, and three to the Air Force.

The glorious list reads as follows:

*OSBORN—C.S.M., W.O. II, John Robert; 1st Bn. The Winnipeg Grenadiers, Hong Kong, 19 December, 1941.

MERRITT—Lieut.-Col. Charles Cecil Ingersoll; The South Saskatchewan Regiment; France, 19 August, 1942.

FOOTE—Hon. Major, John Weir; Canadian Chaplain Service, attached The Royal Hamilton Light Infantry (Wentworth Regiment); France, 19 August, 1942.

*PETERS—Capt., Frederick Thornton; Royal Navy; West Africa, 8 November, 1942.

TRIQUET—Capt. (A/Maj.), Paul; Royal 22e Regiment; Italy, 14 December, 1943.

*HOEY—Capt. (Temp. Maj.), Charles Ferguson; The Lincolnshire Regiment (British Army); Burma, 16 February, 1944.

MAHONEY—Major, John Keefer; The Westminster Regiment (Motor); Italy, 24 May, 1944.

*HORNELL—Flt. Lieut., David Ernest; R.C.A.F.; North Atlantic, 28 July, 1944.

BAZALGETTE—A / Sqd.-Ldr., Ian Willoughby, R.A.F.; France, 4 August, 1944.

CURRIE—Major, David Vivian; 29th Cdn. Armd. Recce. Regt. (South Alberta Regt.); France, 18-20 August, 1944.

SMITH—Pte., Ernest Alvia; The Seaforth Highlanders of Canada; Italy, 21-22 October, 1944.

*COZENS—Sgt., Aubrey; The Queen's Own Rifles of Canada; Holland, 25 - 26 February, 1945.

TILSTON—Capt. (A/Maj.), Frederick Albert; The Essex Scottish; Germany, 1 March, 1945.

TOPHAM—Cpl., Frederick George; 1st Canadian Parachute Bn.; Germany, 25 March, 1945.

*GRAY—Lieut., Robert Hampton; Royal Canadian Naval Volunteer Reserve; Tokyo Bay, 9 August, 1945.

*MYNARSKI—Pilot Officer, Andrew Charles; Royal Canadian Air Force; France, 12 June, 1944.

*Denotes posthumous award.

Besides the Victoria Cross, there are many honours which may be won by British subjects. They are, briefly, as follows:

The George Cross

Instituted by His Majesty King George VI, on 24 September, 1940. This award is made to civilian men and women who perform acts "of the greatest heroism or of the most conspicuous courage in circumstances of extreme danger", in war or peace. It may be conferred upon members of the fighting services for deeds in circumstances where purely military honours do not apply.

The Distinguished Service Order—D.S.O.
Established in 1886 for rewarding distinguished service in wartime. It is granted to commissioned officers of the Navy, the Army, the Air Force, and the Marines, who have previously been mentioned in dispatches. This award ranked second to the Victoria Cross until the institution of the George Cross, which now precedes it. In September, 1942, it was announced that this award might hereafter be conferred upon officers of the Merchant Navy.

The Distinguished Service Cross—D.S.C.
First instituted, in 1901, as The Conspicuous Service Cross, in recognition of distinguished services on the part of warrant officers or subordinate officers of His Majesty's Naval Services, in the presence of the enemy. It was changed on 14 October, 1914, by King George V, to The Distinguished Service Cross, and was extended to include all Naval and Marine officers below the rank of Lieutenant-Commander. It is the only purely Naval decoration, and is now available to the Merchant Navy.

The Military Cross—M.C.
Instituted on 31 December, 1914, for officers of the rank of Captain and below, and warrant officers in the Army or Air Force. It has been awarded to the Navy under exceptional circumstances involving land operations.

The George Medal—G.M.
Conferred in circumstances similar to those meriting the George Cross, where the services are not sufficiently outstanding to win the Cross. The Medal is therefore more freely awarded than is the Cross, yet it calls for a very high standard of conduct.

The Distinguished Conduct Medal—D.C.M.
Instituted in the year 1845, to be awarded to non-commissioned officers and men of the Army. In January, 1943, airmen of non-commissioned rank became eligible for this award, for distinguished conduct in ground operations.

The Conspicuous Gallantry Medal—C.G.M.
Instituted in 1858, at first for the Crimean War only, to be awarded to petty officers and men of the Navy, and to non-commissioned officers and men of the Marines. Later, in 1874, it was reinstituted and made available for all wars in which the Empire might become engaged. At present, airmen of non-commissioned rank, glider pilots, observers, and other Army personnel are eligible for the award for bravery in air operations, as are women of the Naval Services for gallantry on shore during enemy action.

The Distinguished Service Medal—D.S.M.
Instituted on 14 October, 1914, to be awarded to petty officers and men of the Navy, and to non-commissioned officers and men of the Marines who "may at any time show themselves to the fore in action and set an example of bravery and resource under fire". As in the case of the C.G.M., airmen of non-commissioned rank, glider pilots, observers, and other Army personnel, as well as women of the Naval Services, may receive it.

The Military Medal—M.M.
Instituted by King George V in March, 1916, to be awarded to non-commissioned officers and men of the Army or of the Air Force, for "bravery in the field" (in the case of Air Force personnel this applies to action on the ground), and to women of these Services for devotion to duty under fire.

The Great War, 1914-1918, brought into being the Air Force. It was first called the Royal Flying Corps. In the Second World War it became known as The Royal Air Force (in Canada, the Royal Canadian Air Force). It seemed only fitting that this new and daring Service should have its own special honours. Therefore, on 3 June, 1918, four new decorations were instituted by King George V. These four are listed as:

The Distinguished Flying Cross—D.F.C.
The rules of award of this were published in the *London Gazette,* 5 December, 1919, and stated that the Cross might be granted to officers and warrant officers of the Air Corps for acts "of valour, courage, or devotion to duty performed whilst flying in active operations against the enemy".

The Air Force Cross—A.F.C.
Awarded to officers and warrant officers of the Air Services who perform acts of valour or devotion to duty while flying, even though not in active engagement with the enemy. This may be won also by individuals who render special service, in actual flying, to the cause of aviation, whether or not they are attached to the Air Services.

The Distinguished Flying Medal—D.F.M.
Granted to non-commissioned officers and men of the Air Services under the same conditions as those required for the award of the D.F.C. to officers.

The Air Force Medal—A.F.M.
Awarded, like the Air Force Cross, to non-commissioned officers and men of the Air Force, and to individuals who render service to aviation under the same conditions in which the A.F.C. is awarded to officers and warrant officers.

The winner of any of these awards may use the initials of the decoration after his name.

In the Second World War Canada assumed new status in nationhood by declaring war in her own separate right of parliament for the first time. It followed that as a Nation this country should establish her own awards in recognition of valiant deeds. Gradually a system of such awards and decorations was built up over the years from 1943 to 1972.

The Canada Medal—Approved by King George VI and the Canadian Cabinet, 14 October, 1943, "for the recognition of meritorious service by citizens of Canada, whether civilians or members of the armed forces or of the Merchant Navy, and of citizens of other countries who have rendered valuable and meritorious services".

In Canada's Centennial Year, 1967, the Canadian Government introduced a system of honours to take precedence over all awards other than the Victoria Cross and the George Cross.

The Order of Canada (and Companions)—Instituted 17 April, 1967, for outstanding merit of the highest degree in service to Canada or humanity at large.

The Order of Canada—Medal of Courage—Instituted 17 April, 1967, for acts of conspicuous courage in circumstances of great danger, and may be awarded posthumously.

The Order of Canada—Medal of Service—Instituted 17 April, 1967, for service to Canada and limited to fifty awards in any one year.

The Canadian Centennial Medal 1967—Issued on the occasion of the one hundredth Anniversary of the Confederation of Canada in recognition of valuable service to the nation.

The Order of Merit—Created 1 July, 1972, to provide a means of recognition of conspicuous merit and exceptional service by regular and reserve members of the Forces. The Chief of the Defence Staff is, ex-officio, the Principal Commander of the Order.

So it may be seen that men and women who dare to risk their lives in service to their King, their Country, and their fellow-men, are remembered gratefully and in honour. The Canadian scroll of glory is long indeed. Yet there are many heroes not recorded upon it who perform deeds just as glorious, and sacrifice just as much, but receive no material badge or reward. Perhaps these deeds are performed where no earthly eye is there to see; or perhaps, for some reason, no report reaches the ear of authority.

The simple beauty of the Victoria Cross, or the gleam of a lesser medal, is, after all, but a symbol of honour, a reflection of greatness. The splendour of the greatness that lies within the soul of a hero, whether his gallantry has received official recognition or not, will live forever.

THE BRIDGE AT DIEPPE

I

ONE WARM night in August, 1942, a great convoy of ships slipped quietly through the dark waters of the English Channel. This convoy was heading for the town of Dieppe, at that time a German stronghold, on the coast of France. The ships carried soldiers, mostly Canadians, who were going to make a surprise raid on this one-time gay seaside resort.

Two great transport ships, well up front, were crowded with men of the South Saskatchewan Regiment. On one of these, the *Princess Beatrix,* the commanding officer, Lieutenant-Colonel Cecil Merritt, a young lawyer from Vancouver, talked to his men, telling them of the coming great operation.

Everyone listened eagerly. They had learned through months of hard training, in England, that Colonel Merritt was an officer who would not ask his men to go where he would not lead. He was always ready to share with them every danger and hardship. So on this dark night they trusted him and gave him their full attention.

"Well, men, we've trained hard and long for this moment. Soon we are going to use that training against the enemy."

The men were silent. Only the subdued ship-sounds, and the wash of the Channel waters, murmured through the dark.

The Colonel pointed ahead through the gloom.

"See those little green lights winking every once in a while? They are lighted buoys dropped by our mine-sweepers to show us where the way is clear and safe from German mines; clear and safe for us to carry out the plan made in strictest secrecy by the Allied leaders."

He went on to explain that although the shore-line of France was mostly rock and cliffs, the town of Dieppe was situated at a break in the rugged coast. Here the Germans had set up great grim-looking guns, whose dark mouths projected out over the Channel.

Besides wishing to destroy these guns, the Allied leaders had other good reasons for the attack. It was necessary to test the enemy defences, and to try out our own fighting strength.

"Each regiment, each group and each man has a job to do. The South Saskatchewans will land at the village of Pourville, about a mile and a quarter from Dieppe. We must rush the gun-posts there, and push on through the village, clearing the town for the Queen's Own Cameron Highlanders of Canada who will come after us. Every man will find plenty to do, and I know he will do it right. So good luck, lads. This is It."

Wordlessly, but with fast-beating hearts, the soldiers turned once again to checking their weapons. Silence hung in darkness over the ship, but it was a silence filled with the alertness of wakeful, watchful men. Canadians were on their way to a first clash in force with the foe.

About seven-thirty the men crowded below decks for tea, talking and laughing together. Later they gathered in groups to study maps of Dieppe and Pourville. They spoke of many things—some far away, like home and family, some much closer, like the coming day. Few, if any, slept.

The Colonel stood at the deck rail. Once he thought he heard gun-fire from across the water. Then all was quiet again but for the steady thud, thud of the ship's engines. The night was inky black, except for the far-off twinkle of a few stars. He knew that all around him loomed the shadowy outlines of many other craft, all filled with soldiers. There were commandos, their faces blackened, in special motor launches and motor gun-boats; tank men in tank landing-craft, and more infantry men in huge transports. Those in command of the raid watched tensely from the bridges of the destroyers protecting the smaller craft, and up ahead plunged the minesweepers. But here, close around him were *his* men, men whom he knew and who knew him and would follow him. What would the morrow bring? He could not know, and did not dream that, before night came again, those of his men who still lived would speak his name with shining pride.

At a quarter-past four, in the hush and shadows just before dawn, the men climbed silently over the side of the big ship. One by one they dropped into the bobbing small boats, to be carried in to shore. No voices were heard; strict silence was the order. But sailors waiting behind on shipboard whispered hoarsely to soldiers.

"Cheerio, lads. Give 'em a walloping!"

Just off-shore the small craft, which had been going steadily forward, one behind the other in two columns, began to fan out. Soon a straight row stretched parallel to the beach. Then the muffled throbbing of the engines stopped. Not even the wash of the waves at the bows must be allowed to betray them to the enemy.

But what was that beating in the dark overhead? The roar of British bombers coming in on time to prepare the way, and distract the enemy's attention. From the landing-craft the soldiers watched with swiftly-beating hearts. The enemy anti-aircraft guns on shore growled to life. Tracer bullets streaked into the air like fiery comets, picked out their targets and followed the bombers inland. Behind, in the dissolving gloom, the line of boats drifted silently towards shore.

As the square barges nosed into shallow water, the crouching men sprang from their places and ran up onto the shore. The clatter of gun-fire, still following the bombers, sounded farther inland. Still, the only noise on the beach, besides the twittering of wakened birds, was the crunch, crunch of heavy boots on the pebbles. The Saskatchewans were going in exactly on time.

As the men swarmed across the beach they came to a stone wall about twelve feet high. This wall was there to keep the great sea waves from dashing over the village streets in times of storm. Now, the Germans had heavy barbed-wire entanglements strung all along the top of it.

Ladders, brought along for just this purpose, were put up to the wall. The men set quickly to work with their wire-cutters and soon, by twos and threes and dozens, they were over the wall and into the streets of the village. Still there was no sign that the Germans knew of their approach, although the earth shivered with the roar of the great guns firing at the aircraft overhead. The wavering night shadows were streaked with flaming arcs made by the glowing tracer bullets used to guide the gunners to their targets.

"Just like the fireworks on the good old First of July!" quipped one boy, snipping furiously at a tangle of barbed wire in his path.

Just as Colonel Merritt, with the men of Battalion Headquarters, reached the street beyond the parapet, the direction of the German fire changed. Instead of whining over their heads, shells began to burst on the beach and in the streets close by. The spang-g-g of snipers' bullets filled their ears. The Saskatchewans had been sighted by the enemy.

Crouching, running, the men took shelter in the houses along the way. Battalion Headquarters was set up in a big resort hotel. The wireless sets were soon working and the Colonel was giving his steady orders as machine-guns racketed around him. Carefully he looked over the situation, applying to it the knowledge learned from his maps.

Houses lined the streets and water-front, and from upstairs windows of many of those houses German snipers sent forth a ceaseless hail of fire. The main street, leading through the town, stretched away from the hotel to the left; and beyond a slight bend there ran a small stream called the River Scie. The ground sloped upward and on the slopes and higher cliffs were strong enemy gun-posts. And down below were the Canadians, not only under the shadow of the terrible guns in the hills, but swept by the bullets of the unseen snipers from every wall and window.

It was still dark in the village, although the dawn was breaking. The Canadians pushed on up the road through the town. It was a battle of swift movement, from house to house, hedge to hedge. Over it all was the constant bark of the rifles, the thunderous roar of the big guns on the hills, and the sudden bursts of fire here and there from incendiary bullets.

As the South Saskatchewans pushed farther along the main street, they came to the concrete bridge crossing the River Scie. Beyond the slope, and overlooking the bridge, were two machine-gun posts, one above the other, which had to be captured or put out of action. To do this, the bridge must be crossed, of course, and the way cleared for the Camerons, who would be coming in any time now.

The men rushed up on to the bridge. The enemy guns spurted death. Some of the Canadians fell wounded, some were killed. The others tried to take aim at those savage gun-posts. The German guns spoke again. More Canadians dropped on the bridge. Those still unhurt paused, turned, and went back to the shelter of a courtyard partly protected by a large building.

Again they tried it. Hidden snipers picked off more of them as they approached the bridge. Some of the men plunged into the stream, wading and swimming, but the shallow water was soon dotted with broken bodies. Some few reached the other side in safety. Still up there, those hateful, pitiless guns were raking the bridge with bitter fire.

Back in the hotel, Colonel Merritt, returning from the action in the town, heard the wireless operator's report.

"D Company seems to be having trouble, sir. Down at the bridge."

The Colonel listened for a moment, then strode out once more into the streets now flooded with daylight and with a glare even more fiery than the colours of dawn.

In the courtyard near the bridge, the men were crouching, gallantly trying again and again to cross the bridge. As they fired desperately at the threatening guns, Colonel Merritt dashed into the courtyard.

"What's wrong, fellows?" he asked.

"It's those guns overlooking the bridge, sir. We can't seem to make it."

The Colonel looked about, scanning the bridge, the enemy gun-posts, the stream blocked with soldiers' bodies. His jaw set grimly. Taking off his helmet, he swung it lightly in his hand and walked towards the bridge.

"Come on, men," he said: "They can't hit us all."

Twirling his tin hat, he walked out onto the bridge, calling as he went, "See, there's no danger here!"

One by one, by twos and threes, then in large groups, his men followed him, running at first, and crouching low.

"Straighten up, men," the Colonel cried, motioning with his helmet.

One large band crossed in safety. The Colonel walked back across the bridge. The gun-fire did not lessen, rather it seemed to increase. Yet only the climbing sun touched the bright hair of the young officer.

Back in the courtyard, he spoke to the soldiers still hestitating there.

"Spread out," he said "Don't bunch up. We'll make it."

Again he crossed. Again his men followed.

Six times back and forth, with bullets whining and spitting at him, and bursting shells deafening him, Colonel Merritt crossed the bridge.

"We've got to get those Jerries out of there," the Colonel said.

"Well, let's go!" cried the men.

So, armed with smoke bombs, the men rushed towards the pill-box. Under cover of the smoke, they dashed to ground just below the gun-post. Inch by inch, they

Twirling his tin hat, he walked out onto the bridge, calling as he went, "See, there's no danger here!"

crawled up towards it. The Colonel and two sergeants reached it first. Three arms jerked swiftly; three hand-grenades sailed into the pill-box. There was a great burst of flame, and those guns would thunder no more.

Suddenly, during a brief lull in the firing, someone said sharply.

"Listen! What's that?"

High and shrill above the tumult came the skirl of the pipers playing the "March of the Cameron Men". The Camerons were coming in, their way cleared by Colonel Merritt and his South Saskatchewans.

It was getting close to the time set for withdrawal. Colonel Merritt crossed back over the bridge to report that the position had been taken, and to give the order for return to the beach.

It was nearly eleven o'clock when the code word ordering the return to the boats was sent out over the wireless sets. Step by step, the Saskatchewans fought their way back through the village.

Reaching the sea-wall, they began scrambling over it onto the beach below. But the landing-craft had not yet been able to get in to shore, and from the cliff above, another big enemy gun blasted the beach.

The men clung to the slight shelter of the wall and waited. At last the boats began to come in. Out on the open beach, Colonel Merritt knelt by the wireless set and ordered the movement to the boats. The wounded went first, walking if they were able, carried by their comrades if not.

"Fifty more to the boats. Run for it, men!" the order was shouted.

Squish!— Another shell from the gun-post in the cliff ploughed the sand. Pieces of shrapnel, mingled with pebbles, flew wildly among the retreating men.

Colonel Merritt left the wireless set. His face was bleeding from a gash somewhere, but he mopped it with the back of his hand.

"Who'll come with me to knock out that gun?" he called.

One of his majors and a lieutenant followed instantly. Rat-tat-tat sputtered the enemy gun. The men, dodging and bending double, reached the pill-box. There was a sharp burst of noise and sudden fire. The black mouth was quiet, and behind its ruins German gunners sprawled dead.

The crowded boats plunged outwards towards the waiting transports. To the last men leaving the beach Colonel Merritt called, "Good luck!" But he made a vow to the hot, blue August sky to avenge with his last strength what had been done to his men.

All boats not destroyed or crippled headed into the early afternoon sunshine, towards the English cliffs. Over them, through the lifting battle smoke, drummed a heavy air escort. For those on board, the great day was over. But not all were on board.

Many were still in smoking Pourville. With them was Colonel Merritt, now wounded in the leg as well as in the face. Exhausted, they fought on until nearly three o'clock. At last, with ammunition gone, it had to be surrender.

Weeks later in a German prison camp, a private letter from home brought great news to Canadian officers who were prisoners-of-war. Lieutenant Colonel Charles Cecil Ingersoll Merritt had been awarded the Empire's highest honour, the Victoria Cross, for those never-to-be-forgotten hours at Dieppe.

There were no loudly cheering crowds to carry the hero shoulder-high. No flags waved and no bands played. But perhaps the young Colonel preferred simply to have his loyal comrades, who had shared with him the danger on that early morning in August, slapping him on the shoulder.

"Good show, old man," they said, crowding around him, and shaking his hand. They made no fancy speeches, yet in their hearts, they echoed the words of the official citation:

"For matchless gallantry . . . ."

NO HEROES PLEASE

II

At the end of an interview with a former flying officer of the R.C.A.F., No. 1 Fighter Squadron, concerning that unit's part in the Battle of Britain—the officer asserted that he and his colleagues were "only ordinary men doing a necessary job reasonably well", adding the caution—"No heroes, please".

It was a warm day of that unusually sunny summer over England in 1940. In a dispersal hut at an air field just outside of London two Canadian airmen were writing letters home to Montreal. The men in their early thirties were Flying Officers of "A" Flight of the original No. 1 Fighter Squadron, R.C.A.F., first Canadian air unit to fight in the Second World War.

Letter writing was difficult. There were so many things to be said and so much that must be left unsaid. Yet skies over Britain were more than ordinarily clear and the land lay quiet in the sun. People went about with stoical contempt for Adolf Hitler's boast that his Luftwaffe could dispose of Britain's air defence in four days. Still these were fearfully critical days. Dunkirk had taken its heavy toll. France had fallen. Hitler "reasoned" with Britain urging surrender and so avoid inevitable invasion, declaring his intention to eliminate England as a base for operations against him and, if necessary, to occupy the island nation.

"The Battle of France is over ... the Battle of Britain is about to begin. Upon this battle depends the survival of Christian civilization", Churchill warned the nation.

Yet newspapers advertised pleasant summer holiday spots and summer wear. People were, seemingly, more upset over tea rationing which had come into effect on July 9, and what was thought to be a decline in the quality of beer than over bombs on Dover. The airmen from Canada, however, knew the tension that lay beneath the deliberate and courageous belittlement of the situation.

"The Londoners were brave, and they went on being brave for a long time", was one famous comment of that year.

And such was the quality of fortitude shared by the newly arrived Canadians who also, in doing a job they saw as desperately necessary, went on being brave for a long time. The two letter-writers and their comrades of No. 1 Fighter Squadron were members of one of the most unique groups in the history of Canadian air-warfare. Not much over a year earlier these two and others like them had been at the beginning of successful business careers in Montreal. Keen alike in work and in offtime sports and interests, the common factor which had brought them from their promising positions to this endangered island was their interest and participation in planes and flying.

Prior to the Second World War quite separate groups of young men were keenly interested in the comparatively new and exciting world of air flight. Among these was Auxiliary Squadron in Westmount, Quebec, 115 Squadron, which operated Fleet aircraft at St. Hubert. There was, as well, a No. 1 Fighter Squadron of the permanent R.C.A.F., and there were the young business men already established in responsible careers, who held, in common with the other groups, an interest in aircraft and the science of flying them. These were members of the Montreal Light Aeroplane Club. The letter-writers in the dispersal hut, with a few others, were of this civilian group.

Adolf Hitler continued his death-strewn march against peace and freedom and Europe was littered with his broken promises. Thinking men watched with horror this evil let loose in the world.

For permanent force and auxiliary squadron pilots, war and their own participation in it, was always a possible, though, perhaps, little expected consequence. By nature of their chosen field most of these very young and daring flyers were adventurous, eager, pioneering in the thrilling world of boundless space. The glamour and excitement beckoned to others of their age group over Canada. Eager to fight for their country these lads flocked to the newest arm of the service, the Air Force.

With the maturity of their few added years and broader experience the civilian flyers of the Montreal Light Aeroplane Club saw a grimmer prospect. They were keen, young but not youths, looking enthusiastically to the years ahead, good and useful lives, were it not for the menace that grew and spread. They watched this evil as it crept month by month over Europe, its traditions, its culture—and its peace. This must not continue. Filled with firm conviction, as men and Canadians they must do their part. Accordingly, leaving the life they knew and wanted to preserve, these men offered their services where they felt most competent—in the air.

Soon after the declaration of war in September 1939, these three groups, far apart in actual distance, in experience and in outlook, came together as one in singleness of purpose, and a new, No. 1 Fighter Squadron, Royal Canadian Air Force assumed its war strength. This unit was the first Royal Canadian Air Force Squadron to fight in the Second World War. Its experience as its composition was unique, war in the air being in its infancy and quite different from 1914-1918. No. 1 Fighter Squadron went to England in early June 1940, to take part in the epic Battle of Britain, the most historic battle of modern times, as a unit in Britain's Fighter Command, R.A.F.

The No. 1 Squadron took with them their single-seater monoplane Hurricanes in which they had trained in Canada, but that training was of the most elementary and brief in time. But time was then something the world did not have. Time for the way of life we knew was running out.

Posted to a base south of London, No. 1 Squadron was drilled in the essentials of air warfare. Their older model Hurricanes were replaced, with their eight guns forward, capable of a speed of 335 miles per hour, and now equipped with self-sealing tanks, armour plating, and variable pitch propellers.

Meanwhile the Battle of Britain was approaching its critical stage.

In the dispersal hut on base, where the two Montreal men were writing letters home, two of the younger air-force pilots came into the far end of the building. The older men paid little attention until they were the subject of the boys' talk. It appeared that the youths had begun, perhaps for the first time, to look into the uncertain future and its hazards.

"Why do you suppose those old fellows got into this", puzzled the boys, obviously referring to the letter-writers, "they didn't need to come?"

To the wry amusement of the thirty-odd year "old men" the youngsters decided that since these senior airmen already had lived their lives, at their age it couldn't really matter much to them what happened. After all what was left of any importance for them? Maturity was not yet a word in the usual pilot age-group of approximately eighteen to twenty-six. So it came about that three greatly differing groups of men acted as one, a team with balance provided by those very differences, complementing each other, comrades-at-arms in a common cause.

By now, every day morning and afternoon, saw great waves of 200 to 300 German bombers fanning out over the English channel approaching the ports, towns and cities of England. Breaking into groups of 20 or more they flew over pre-determined targets dropping their deadly loads.

For the officers and crews of No. 1 Squadron the days took on a new and extraordinary routine. Roused at 4 a.m. the pilots swallowed hot tea, pulled on their flying suits, and went to their day's work— an odd day's work —three or four or five miles above the earth alone in a frail world of strut and steel. Patrolling the skies was, at first, the extent of their involvement as the Squadron had been moved to a base to the west of London. In this position they were just on the fringe of the fiercest battle line as enemy action was concentrated first on shipping and the southern ports. This patrol duty did not last long.

It was a Saturday, in late summer when No. 1 went out as usual on its first patrol of the day at 4 o'clock in the morning. The day began like other days but at its end the story was forever changed.

As the Squadron flew over London the sky above the Thames Estuary was darkened by file after file of fearsome black German bombers flying in their usual "V" formation. It was a never-to-be-forgotten sight to the Canadians, their first actual brush with the enemy of world peace. Outnumbered five to one, and outsized by the huge bombers, the Hurricanes flew straight into the mass of ugly enemy craft. There were bad moments. There were exciting moments. Every Canadian plane flew straight for the bombers, all eight guns blazing, scattering the order of the German formation. One flying officer found himself entirely surrounded by the Nazi planes. It was a grim moment. But with a burst of speed the pilot flew straight up, up out of the mass and on, to deliver his gunfire down on the bombers below him.

Four German aircraft were destroyed by the Squadron that first day in battle action, and as many more damaged. The Squadron lost one pilot and two other Hurricanes were shot down forcing the pilots to bale out and parachute to safety. Many others suffered lesser damage.

But the great day for the Canadian Squadron as for all

the air defenders of Britain was September 15, 1940. The Battle of Britain has been officially dated from July 10 to October 31, that year, but the most historic and decisive day was that fifteenth day of September.

Hitler had fixed on September 21 as the most suitable day for Operation Zero, invasion of Britain. In preparation for this event the Luftwaffe hurled its blackest might of destruction on the little island. Day after day, the Hurricanes of No. 1 Squadron joined the Fighter Command's total air war.

That fateful morning dawned bright with a slight haze which cleared about noon. At first it seemed like just another day "on the job" to the pilots of No. 1. Just before noon the Tannoy (public address system between operations room and dispersal hut) alerted the men ... "Scramble, Angels—20", the order to action at 20,000 feet.

The Hurricanes flew out to meet the biggest air attack so far. Flying in V formation came wave after wave of German bombers, with their fighter escorts above, behind, and all around them. Over the Channel, over the southern ports, over the shipping in harbour, on they came, target London at the heart of Britain. As Big Ben struck the hour of twelve mid-day, several formations had broken through the defending aircraft of Fighter Command by sheer force of numbers, and were flying over the outskirts of the city.

In and out among the death-dealing craft darted the Hurricanes, guns blasting with telling effect. This battle was sharp and short, but the day was not over for London, for Fighter Command or for Canadian No. 1 Fighter Squadron. About 2.30 p.m. the Squadron was called out again and yet again. On that gruelling day the group went up five times in all.

Flying over the south end of London the Hurricane pilots saw an advancing mass of German aircraft. Other Squadrons of the Command were already attacking, so No. 1 flew higher and on to find their own quarry. It was not hard to find. Over one hundred bombers surrounded by their own fighter escort advanced on the smoking city. No. 1 Squadron acting with their notable team work closed with the bombers, leaving the fighters to their comrade squadrons, Polish and English.

The sky was crowded with aircraft. It was like some terrible air traffic jam filled with sound and fury, danger and death. More than a thousand planes, foe and defender, shut out the sunshine in the sky just south of London. Bomber after bomber went down in flames. Parachutes from stricken planes added to the air congestion. The single-manned Hurricanes left in action went about their grim business.

Presently the German planes turned, by ones, by twos, by threes, towards the Channel and their bases in France. The Hurricanes of No. 1 Squadron flew home, singly, their pilots weary, war-sick, but satisfied they had done a necessary job "reasonably well". How well was "reasonably" is now historical fact.

On that early fall day in 1940, now officially known as Battle of Britain Day, the enemy lost over London 185 planes. Of this number the R.C.A.F. No. 1 Fighter Squadron accounted for fourteen. Never again did Goring's Luftwaffe come in such numbers and confidence over England. And Hitler's Operation Zero became one with his other mad, lost dreams.

Of No. 1 Fighter Squadron, the Honourable C. G. Power, minister of National Defence for Air at that time, said:

> "While the Battle of Britain raged in the skies from August 1940, until late Autumn, these lads were in the thick of it. They showed the precision of a star Canadian hockey team...".

"THE TEAM"

THE ORIGINAL R.C.A.F No 1 FIGHTER SQUADRON. Ranks as at beginning of War. Decorations and casualties as at end of hostilities.

Squadron Leader—Ernest A. McNab, D.F.C.
Commanding Officer

"A" Flight

F/L Gordon R. McGregor, OBE, DFC, commanding
F/O Hartland de M. Molson, OBE (wounded)
F/O John W. Kerwin (wounded, killed)
F/O A. Deane Nesbitt, OBE, DFC (wounded)
F/O Beverley E. Christmas
F/O Robert Leslie Edwards (killed)
F/O Paul Pitcher
F/O Ross Smither (killed)
F/O Edwin M. Reyno AFC
F/O Carl Briese

"B" Flight

F/O Vaughan B. Corbett (wounded, killed), commanding
F/O Eric Beardmore (wounded)
F/O Jean-Paul Desloges—Legion d'Honneur (wounded, killed)
F/O George G. Hyde (wounded, killed)
F/O Thomas B. Little (wounded, killed)
F/O Otto Jean Peterson (wounded, killed)
F/O Blair Dalzell Russell, DSO, DFC, and Bar
F/O William B. Sprenger (killed)
F/O Arthur M. Yuile (wounded)

GRAPNEL GERMANY

III

ON A certain grim day in September, 1939, a strange, brief message was flashed to all ships in the Royal Canadian Navy. *Grapnel Germany!* When this two-word despatch was deciphered, it read: "The nation, side by side with Britain, is at war with Germany, and enemy forces are to be engaged and put out of action."

Accordingly, with dauntless spirit, the small strength of the young Canadian Navy gathered itself against the foe.

So it came about that three years later, on the second day of August, 1942, a convoy of grey ships headed for mid-ocean, outward from St. John's Newfoundland.

This particular group of seagoing vessels was called for official purposes S.C (Slow Convoy) 94, and was being escorted according to the system then used by Allied Naval authorities. This system of guarding the sea-lanes against lurking enemy submarines assigned a number of protecting warships to each assemblage of unarmed ships. The warships formed an "escort group". At this time such a group was usually made up of ships from the British and Canadian Navies.

A local escort convoyed ships from Halifax to St. John's, Newfoundland. At St. John's another force relieved the local escort and took the convoy all the way across the North Atlantic to British waters. There it was met and in turn relieved by a small force coming out from the United Kingdom to guide the ships into port.

On this August 2, an escort group of the Newfoundland Escort Force, consisting of four Canadian and three British warships, took over S.C. 94 at St. John's and convoyed it seawards. Among them was the H.M.S. *Assiniboine,* a destroyer.

In the wheel-house, Acting Chief Petty Officer Max Bernays steered the *Assiniboine* through a thick fog rolling in from the sea. From time to time orders came from the bridge, and the ship responded under the Chief Petty Officer's able guidance. Beside him stood two telegraph men, ready to relay orders from the bridge throughout the ship. It was quiet in the wheel-house—a silence of which the muffled, persistent grinding of engines seemed part, and which was broken only by the orders from the bridge —quiet in comparison with the friendly hubbub of downtown New Westminster, British Columbia, where Max Bernays had grown up. But he was too engrossed in his duties to spare time for memories.

The long columns of cargo ships wavered through the fog. Here and there the heavy grey curtain lifted to show the outline of another escort ship swinging back to round up a straggler which had lost its way in the mist. The men were at cruising stations: that is to say, only the routine number were at duty posts, while those who would later relieve them relaxed. When the electric bell system rang "Action Stations" throughout the ship, all men would double to duty posts.

Just now, however, as night shadows added their gloom to the drifting fog, all was hushed aboard the destroyer, yet the men were alert for instant action. For this was a dangerous area, during a dangerous period of the war.

Murky dawn brought no relief from the damp, grey blanket that muffled the convoy. H.M.C.S. *Battleford,* one of the escort vessels, dropped behind to guide some straying merchant ships back into line. Plunging about in the eddying whirls of fog, the warship lost its bearings and was finally forced to break wireless silence and communicate with the Senior Officer.

"Bad show, this fog," thought Chief Officer Bernays. "An emergency wireless right now would give us away to any U-boats cruising about."

It was not until the afternoon of the fifth, however, that any real danger threatened. The *Assiniboine* had left her usual place in the convoy and was approaching three or four ships that had wandered out of line. This detour, whose purpose was to bring the stragglers back into protected formation, took the destroyer about three miles distant from the other escort ships. Therefore her first hint of alarm came suddenly when the deadened roar of an explosion thundered through the mist from the convoy up ahead.

"Action Stations!"

The*Assiniboine* swung about under the helmsman's hand.

"S.S. *Spar*——— got it———torpedoed."

Assiniboine nosed through the gloom. To the straining ears of the men on board came the sound of sister ships firing on some furtive enemy.

"Half ahead together."

But though the look-outs on the destroyer scanned the tumbling seas anxiously, no pointing periscope met their gaze. No phantom shape of a U-boat emerged from the fog.

The dark night dragged on with nothing to break the tense watch, beyond a heavy splash somewhere in the shadows nearby. It could have been a U-boat crash-diving. In the light of what happened next day, men on the *Assiniboine* thought that it had been. But the following hours were free from alarms—until shortly after eleven o'clock next morning.

"Object bearing red four-five," was the signal.

"Full ahead together!" came the order from the bridge. A moment later the "object" was seen to be the conning-tower of a U-boat. The battle was on. There was a blasting roar from the guns of *Assiniboine*. The vessel shook with the charges. Three times this was repeated, and the submarine dived beneath the waves. H.M.S. *Dianthus* steamed in to help the *Assiniboine*. Depth charges and explosives rumbled from both ships. But no sign of life—or of death—came from the submerged U-boat.

The men on the destroyer relaxed a little. Perhaps that was all the "show" for this run, they thought. Nevertheless, while eased of some of the tension, the men remained ever on the watch. The tumbling seas and swirling fog would be such an effective cloak for further enemy action.

It was not with surprise, therefore, that the look-out sighted a submarine again, this time at a range of about six miles. Again the chase was on. But the enemy sped away and soon dived beneath the waves.

Upon the bridge, a fully exposed target, the Captain strained his eyes towards the spot where the U-boat had disappeared.

"Now what kind of a game do they think they're playing?" he wondered. "Too close to torpedo us," he decided, squinting across the churning green seas.

"Well, if they think they're going to manoeuvre around till they get a chance to blast us off the ocean and then get away themselves . . ."

He didn't finish the sentence but his determined expression boded ill for the U-boat. He spoke rapidly into the tube leading down to the wheel-house.

Petty Officer Bernays swung the wheel over hard. The telegraph men on either side of him bent to their instruments. The ship forged ahead.

Again the crisp voice sounded down the tube. Again Bernays swung the wheel over, checked his instruments and listened for further instructions.

"So it's going to be hide-and-seek, is it?" he murmured, settling himself more firmly before his wheel, and wondering what the Captain saw as he scanned the heavy seas. He was not left to wonder long.

"Submarine bearing red nine-o fifteen hundred yards."

The message spoken with offcial calm carried tense excitement throughout the ship.

"As close as that, is she? Must be in full view," thought Bernays, changing course, in quick response to the rapid fire of orders from the bridge.

The U-boat *was* in full view on the surface of the water. This time she did not dive. The fog, still whirling and drifting about the convoy, offered cover for a sly attack on the *Assiniboine*. The shadowy raider turned and glided at full speed into the murky shrouds of mist.

It was all too clear that a stealthy foray was planned from the depths of the sheltering fog. In this way the U-boat schemed to destroy the *Assiniboine,* and later perhaps some of the helpless merchant ships, with the minimum of danger to herself.

The only defence was attack. Accordingly the destroyer gave chase. Although the U-boat had lost herself in the wavering haze, the radar equipment on the pursuing ship detected the course of her flight. Nearer and nearer sped the *Assiniboine*. Soon she closed to within one hundred yards of the U-boat. She opened fire. The U-boat answered with a rain of explosives and machine-gun bullets, at the same time dodging about trying to get in close to, and match moves with, the warship.

For this reason the *Assiniboine* could not bring her heavy guns low enough to aim at her agile quarry. Nevertheless the intrepid gun crew, by Captain's orders, kept up the fire.

Their persistence was rewarded, when a direct hit was scored upon the submarine's conning-tower. Amid the resulting confusion on the U-boat men were seen struggling to reach the gun mounted amidships. Another round of explosive belched from the *Assiniboine* and found its mark. The U-boats amidships gun was never fired.

The destroyer was rocking and heeling over from the pounding of her own guns, amid the splatter of fire from the U-boat. Suddenly a flicker and then a burst of flame shot upward from her starboard deck. The shells had found a mark close to the door of the wheel-house. Not far from the tongues of the blaze was a store of ammunition. The greedy flames soared higher and higher, fanning out. The Captain shouted warning orders to the helmsman and telegraph men in the wheel-house.

Meanwhile, Chief Petty Officer Bernays heard the roar and crackle of the flames outside his duty post. The ship was wallowing and shuddering so violently that all his strength was needed to manage the helm. The turmoil thundered about his ears, making it difficult for him to follow the steady flow of orders coming from the bridge. Smoke seeped and eddied into the wheel-house and curled threatening fingers about his head. The telegraph men choked and staggered. Soon the wisps of smoke were sweltering, smothering fingers, clutching and tearing at the throats of the men. The heat of the small room was almost unbearable; the steel-plated walls like the sides of an oven. The telegraph men, flung from their posts, fumbled blindly for the single door, the only escape from searing death.

But the orders still came from the bridge. The battle was still being waged. Whether it was being lost or won, Max Bernays could not know, shut off as he was in his wheel-house. Yet grimly and in stifling torture he gripped his wheel—swung to port—to starboard—following every command. Alone in his seething, smoke-reeking prison, the Chief Petty Officer carried out his own almost impossible duty, and, as well, received and despatched the orders for the two who had been forced from their posts.

From the bridge the Captain watched the rush of movement in the submarine. He saw an officer, who had been standing in the narrow hatch leading to the conning-tower, turn swiftly and descend from his post. The Captain suspected that the U-boat was going to dive. That must not happen, to prolong the danger to his ship and her valuable charges. Instantly he gave orders to ram the submarine. Fraught with danger as this manoeuvre was,

Yet grimly . . . he gripped his wheel
. . . following every command.

it yet remained the only way to foil the cunning strategy of the U-boat.

Down in the inferno of the wheel-house Bernays carried on with his triple task. Sweat poured down his blistering face. Smoke stung his eyeballs cruelly. His lungs burned and his throat filled with the stinging blasts of heat and scorching fumes. Still he clung with failing strength to the wheel. Gasping for a cool breath of air, he swung it over, checked his instruments; then back to the wheel. The *Assiniboine* bore down on the U-boat. Now! The thrust caught the submarine near the conning-tower, towards the stern.

The destroyer shuddered violently, lurched, then righted herself. Bernays was almost flung from his post. But orders were coming from the bridge again. He renewed his grip on the wheel. Steady! The smoke seemed to be clearing a little.

The Captain ordered another lunge at the U-boat. Again the wheel responded: over—back—over—steady ahead. The ship drove towards the partly surfaced submarine. There was a second tremendous impact. The U-boat plunged and leaped in the thrashing waves. Then with a violent lurch she pitched head down into the boiling green waters.

The battle was over—and won. The fire outside the wheel-house had been extinguished. And the helmsman, the urgency of his duty past, breathed more easily, yet his scorched throat and lungs for many hours bore painful witness to his ordeal by fire.

In the words which cited Max Bernays for the Conspicuous Gallantry Medal:

> "The final success of the sinking of the U-boat was largely due to the high courage and determination of Acting Chief Petty Officer Max Leopold Bernays, [who] alone and with complete disregard for his own safety, with flames and smoke obscuring his only exit, with enemy explosive shell fragments

> entering the wheel-house . . . remained at his post for nearly forty minutes . . ."

One more enemy force had been engaged and put out of action. Grapnel Germany!

NOT ON THE LONE PRAIRIE

IV

A WINTRY wind was sweeping down from the prairies. It howled through the streets of Winnipeg, snatching at snowbanks and whirling white flurries high into the air. The comfortable little house where the Osborns lived shuddered with the blast, but inside all was warm and cosy.

"What shall I play now?" asked Mother Osborn at the piano.

"Let's have 'The Cowboy's Lament' again," said her husband.

"Oh, Dad," laughed Fern, "do you never get tired of that old thing?"

"Never mind, Dad, it's a good song. Don't let her kid you," said John.

"Yes, yes, Mom, do play it. I like it, too," chimed in ten-year-old George, while his little sister, Patsy, added, "I do, too, Daddy—you sing it for us."

It was Christmas time and Sergeant-Major John Robert Osborn of the Winnipeg Grenadiers was enjoying a family sing-song around the piano. It was one of the hours this stalwart British-born Canadian liked best. He had come to Canada, after brave and honourable service with British forces in World War 1914-1918. He was not very strong after the War, but he struggled with unwearied courage to make a home for his family.

Now, as the year 1938 drew to a close, he was enjoying that home. Osborn was soldiering again, but in a peacetime world. All was so restful in the little Winnipeg home that Jack Osborn could not dream what Christmas two years later would bring.

His strong voice rang out in the song he liked so well.

" 'Oh bury me not on the lone prairie . . .' "

"Why not?" laughed Jack, when the music stopped. "It's as good a place as any. Anyhow, I figure I'll die with my boots on, wherever it is. It's a good way to die."

"Oh come on, Dad! Who's thinking of dying now? Let's sing."

And the happy family sang on.

Two years later, Jack Osborn, now Company Sergeant-Major, was far from the song and laughter of his Winnipeg home. No whirling eddies of snow blew in cold fury over his head; but great, droning Japanese planes dived and zoomed wickedly above him. No Canadian prairie wind tore at his clothing or screamed in his ears. Instead, there were the high shriek of enemy shells, and the whine of enemy bullets.

The Sergeant-Major was leading his Company of Winnipeg Grenadiers in a desperate battle against the Japs in Britain's far-off island colony of Hong Kong. It was the morning of 19 December, 1941. All the world was sad and anxious with the terrors of war. There was little Christmastide joy in many hearts. In Hong Kong, where men battled for their very lives, there was no time for anything but the desperate fighting.

On one side of this little Company of Grenadiers the sharp slopes of Mount Butler rose steeply above sea-level. On the other side rolled the South China Sea.

"Sergeant-Major, I can't get through to Headquarters," reported the man at the wireless set.

"Well, keep trying, chum," ordered Osborn.

Yet, as he spoke, he feared that it was hopeless. Through the smoke of battle, he peered right and left for a sign of another friendly party. There was none. In fact, only a part of his own Company could be seen. He wiped his eyes with the back of his hand and looked towards Mount Butler. That was the objective of the present battle. To take that bit of rising ground from the enemy would mean much to the hard-pressed Allied troops.

The Sergeant-Major waved to his men.

"Come on, boys. Let's at 'em!" he shouted, fixing his bayonet and plunging forward.

The men rallied around him. Inch by inch, they struggled closer and closer to the foot of the hill. From hiding-places on the slopes, the Jap bullets spattered. Time and again, the gallant little Company staggered back from the overwhelming enemy force holding the hill. Time and again, encouraged and led by their Sergeant-Major, they pressed forward.

Up, up the steep slope, they fought their way, slowly driving the enemy down. Finally, in suffering and loss, the hill was taken. Still, the task of holding it lay ahead of them. The afternoon wore on. Wave after wave of Japanese soldiers crawled up the slopes. The Sergeant-Major and his men met them face to face and forced them back. But the enemy had too many reinforcements. As fast as one group of yellow faces was beaten back, others crept up, in front, behind, and on all sides.

For three dreadful hours the battle raged. At last, the Company Sergeant-Major was forced to admit it was no longer possible to hold the hill. He gathered his remaining men together and ordered withdrawal down the slope. The first few retreated safely to sea-level and were able to join a larger force of Grenadiers there. Sergeant-Major Osborn, with a few men helping him, held back the oncoming Japs until the little group had reached the foot of the hill.

"After them, the rest of you," ordered Osborn, facing alone the still approaching enemy. Dashing from shelter to shelter, from rock to tree, he drew and held the fire to himself, until the last straggler had joined the force below.

"Now for it," Jack Osborn thought, and he sprinted down an open space behind his men. A bullet hummed past his ear.

"Whew-w! That was a near thing." On he went, running, turning to fire into yellow faces, crawling, sliding, rolling. Machine-gun fire burst all around him, throwing up clods of earth. Still, miraculously unhurt, the Sergeant-Major raced on, until at last he breathlessly rejoined his men.

After a brief breathing spell the Companies rallied once more round their leaders. The Sergeant-Major talked heartily and cheerfully to his men. From the small shelter of a little hollow, they took up the fight. The enemy fire was intense but most of it sailed right over the little company, doing no harm.

Beyond the rise, other Grenadiers battled fiercely. Sounds of desperate action reached the ears of Osborn's Company.

"Sounds pretty tough," said the Sergeant-Major, lying flat and peering carefully over the edge of the hollow. Suddenly, he rolled over and scrambled to his feet.

"On guard, men!" he called sharply. The men followed his pointing finger. Beyond the hollow, through the battle smoke, dozens of stocky, slant-eyed little figures ran, crouching low, towards them. Osborn swung to the left. There, too, swarmed the yellow men. They were everywhere! The Company was surrounded, completely cut off from its battalion.

Quickly, the Sergeant-Major rallied his little band. He looked again with great caution over the edge of the hollow. What he saw chilled his racing blood.

Just a few yards away, a stealthy figure squirmed towards the hollow. As the Sergeant-Major watched in sudden alarm, the Jap scrambled to his feet and lifted his arm.

Osborn understood.

"Watch out, men!" he shouted over his shoulder. "Grenades!"

In a flash, the Sergeant-Major . . .
tossed it back towards the enemy.

Even as he spoke, the deadly little bomb left the enemy hand and spun through the air. Seconds later, a loud explosion shook the ground. The grenade had fallen short, however, and no one was hurt—not that time! Almost at once another grenade sailed towards the stricken group. In a flash, the Sergeant-Major darted from his place, snatched at it, straightened up and tossed it back towards the enemy. Again a grenade soared towards him. He repeated his unbelievably quick and gallant action. Again and again, he leaped towards the falling grenades, like a player in a deadly game of ball. Meantime, the members of his Company were holding off the advancing enemy.

Other Companies of Canadians were approaching to aid them. The grim situation might yet be saved. The men, owing their lives to the Sergeant-Major's heroism, took fresh courage and renewed the struggle.

Suddenly, another of the terrible missiles lobbed right into their midst. But it fell in a rocky cleft nearby, where the Sergeant-Major could not reach it in time. Seeing at a glance how matters stood, the valiant soldier, without hesitation, did the only thing that could possibly save the lives of his comrades. Shouting a warning to those who would have gone to his aid, he sprang forward and flung his tall body downward over the grenade.

At that moment it exploded, and the Company Sergeant-Major saved the lives of his men—at the cost of his own.

Back home in Winnipeg, Jack Osborn's wife and family think often of the old sing-songs. They repeat to each other the Sergeant-Major's words: "I figure I'll die with my boots on. It's a good way to die." Company-Sergeant-Major John Robert Osborn's King and countrymen agreed, and the Victoria Cross was awarded posthumously to the man who died that others might live.

SPECIAL DUTY

V

ON A GOLDEN September day in 1940 George Cook, a yacht designer of Lakefield, Ontario, pledged his skill and knowledge of things nautical, to the Royal Canadian Naval Volunteer Reserve, "for the duration". His craftsmanship was sure to be of value in his chosen Service.

But the young acting lieutenant devoted, that day, another and equally valuable quality to the service of his country—a quality that was to be known only in the testing time of gravest peril. This was the quiet, steady courage that sent him out, not once, but repeatedly, to face a horrible death, alone and without fanfare.

Some inkling of this quality must have early shown itself to his superiors, however; for on 10 September, 1940, Lieutenant Cook was appointed overseas to serve on H.M.S. *King Alfred*, a shore base. Here, and subsequently on ships, he was taught among other things, to identify the different types of mines that the enemy strewed so thickly over our most vital sea-lanes.

These cleverly constructed explosives were of several kinds and were detonated in various ways. Many Allied ships of that period steamed, unsuspecting, into a mined area, and without warning were blown to pieces in a welter of spray, their brave crews trapped on board.

To ward off this pressing danger, Mine Disposal Squads were formed and sent forth to seek out, by all means known to science, the deadly mines. But to fight any enemy, one must first learn wherein lies his strength. And therefore, combating this particular sea terror meant not only locating and destroying mines, but taking them apart —or "stripping" them—to find out how they worked. To such hazardous duty, then, did George Cook devote his skill and courage.

With others in his group, he learned to identify the known types of mine. But that did not satisfy this lieutenant so keen in his job. He took great pains to learn all the details of the complicated mechanisms: why such a one exploded when it did; why such another did not when expected; why a certain one, seemingly "dead", suddenly burst in the faces of those who were stripping it.

After some months of this careful research and study, Acting Lieutenant George Cook was attached to the Staff of the Senior British Naval Officer in the Suez Canal area.

On 24 February, 1941, a German parachute mine was sighted. There were none of the trained service divers at hand to go into action against the mine. At any moment, it might explode. Lieutenant Cook acted quietly, but without delay. None knew better than he, who had studied the fiendish mechanism, the fearful risk he was taking. He did not hesitate.

Carefully, tensely, he cast a net over the floating horror. With infinite patience, he drew the thing into shallow water, foot by dangerous foot.

"There! So far so good," he must have thought. Yet the task was only begun. To remove the poisonous sting from the serpent, one must draw the fangs. So it was with the mine. Only when the fuse was removed, would it be harmless.

Lieutenant Cook set to work. The monstrous black object had to be neutralized under water. So, while strained minutes ticked by, the Lieutenant's skilled, steady hands busied themselves with the deadly mechanism.

It was done! Surely the man could call it a job com-

With infinite patience, he drew the thing into shallow water, foot by dangerous foot.

pleted and send it away, its fangs drawn. But no! Who knew, he reasoned, what other menace lurked hidden in its cold iron heart? Besides, taking it apart to examine it more closely would certainly add to the useful information so sorely needed.

Accordingly, Cook sought and obtained permission to work further on the mine. He had it drawn by lorry far into the desert. Here, in solitude, he worked for five days. But, although he worked alone, not one of his most minute discoveries was lost to the authorities. For in Mine Disposal work, as in Bomb Disposal, the worker reports each tiny operation through a wireless set or phone. So, if in making a certain adjustment he should say, "I am about to do such and such . . ." and his listeners should next hear a deafening roar, then silence, they would know that the mine had been set off by the action described in those last words.

In this case, however, five days of such strain and peril brought happy results. The mine was completely stripped. Its element was withdrawn and sent home for expert study.

Lieutenant Cook, exhausted as he must have been, knowing full well that he faced death every hour of those five days, had rendered a great service. It was the first time in World War II that a mine had been successfully recovered from water deep enough to arm it, and stripped without loss of life. For this outstanding service, Lieutenant Cook was awarded the George Medal—although no streaming headlines bore the news to an admiring world.

Quietly, George Cook continued his dangerous duties. No flash and whirl of battle surrounded him. The surge of supreme effort, in the headlong excitement of action, did not come to his aid. For his was the unheralded, everyday service behind the front lines.

Months passed, a New Year dawned, and February came again. On 10 February, 1942, a mine was dropped on the shore at Haifa. Lieutenant Cook took charge. Calmly he examined it.

"This is a G mine," he pronounced. "Normally it should have exploded, since it was not under water."

It was a fearful moment. There lay the monstrous thing that ought to have exploded! Who knew at what second it might do so? There was only one thing to do, according to Lieutenant Cook. It must be stripped on the spot, and at once. There was only one person to do it, decided Lieutenant Cook. That person was George Cook.

The scene immediately became one of intense action. The Lieutenant snapped out sharp orders.

"The area must be cleared. All people within dangerous distance evacuated. Give the word and get busy."

"Right, sir."

Fourteen thousand people hurried away to places of safety. While they were being shepherded out of harm's way, the Lieutenant had a tent pitched over the mine. Around the tent, sandbags were stacked to break the force of an explosion if one occurred.

Presently, when all was ready, George Cook walked calmly into the enclosure. Pushing aside the tent flap, he stepped under it and, letting it fall behind him, disappeared from view.

While nervous watchers waited, the Lieutenant adjusted his head-set and started to work. Quietly his voice began reporting every detail of his work on the mine.

"It is as I thought. This type of mine is sensitive to light and must be worked on in almost total darkness . . .

"It is difficult to work with any speed; going by touch only . . ."

So, for three and a half breathless hours, George Cook carried out his operation on the mine. Small wonder if his fingers fumbled a little, or his hands faltered over their task. For the mine was a strange one to him, and many times a turn to the right instead of the left might have brought instantaneous death upon him. But if his fingers faltered, his nerve did not fail him, nor did his steadfast purpose flicker.

And presently the work was done. The Lieutenant drew

a deep breath, pulled off the head-set and stumbled out into the daylight.

Another magnificent duty had been carried out, another battle won against the evil forces of destruction, and still no banners waved nor trumpets sounded.

A man had completed a task. And if that task called for superb daring, intrepid skill, and steadfast heart, only those who waited beyond the tent and the sandbags knew how fully the call had been met. And grateful officialdom added a Bar to Lieutenant Cook's George Medal.

Secrecy, for safety's sake, surrounded much of the work undertaken by Lieutenant Cook. So he continued in his work, which was listed as "Special Duty", with the British Admiralty.

As the months went by, other honours came to George Cook. Finally, in January, 1945, he was confirmed in the rank of Lieutenant-Commander, and the following July he was Mentioned in Despatches.

After Canada's first peacetime Christmas in six years, Lieutenant-Commander George Cook returned to his home in Lakefield.

No doubt confidential reports tell precisely and briefly of George Cook's work done in secret and in danger. Yet imagination cannot paint, nor words describe, the horrors of those long, long hours on "Special Duty".

THE HAPPY WARRIOR

VI

"Who is the happy Warrior? Who is he
That every man in arms should wish to be?
—It is the generous Spirit, who, when brought
Among the tasks of real life, hath wrought
Upon the plan that pleased his boyish thought:
"Who, doomed to go in company with Pain,
And Fear, and Bloodshed, miserable train!
Turns his necessity to glorious gain.
"Whom neither shape of danger can dismay,
Nor thought of tender happiness betray;
Who, not content that former worth stand fast,
Looks forward, persevering to the last,
From well to better, daily self-surpast."

From "Character of the Happy Warrior"
WILLIAM WORDSWORTH

IN A CERTAIN modern dictionary there is quite an interesting definition of the word "bravery". The attempt is made to compare the word with others often used in place of it, such as "courage" or "valour". These fine words have power to kindle our imaginations to thoughts of noble deeds and gallant men and women. Perhaps, indeed, we are used to thinking of all these expressions as having exactly the same meaning. Yet this dictionary tells us that "courage" is the noblest term of all. It goes on to explain that bravery is often present at the moment of danger when blood runs fast with excitement, and is more common than courage. For courage is that quality which meets dangers, trials, and emergencies conquering fear under all circumstances.

This story is about a man who has courage.

In the days before the Second World War, there lived near the broad blue of the St. Lawrence River a young man who was keenly interested in many things. Dwelling with his family in Cornwall, Ontario, home of the famous "Kiltie" Regiment, the Stormont, Dundas, and Glengarry Highlanders, Allan Piper thrilled to the skirl of the Pipe Band and joined the peacetime formation of the Regiment. Only seventeen at the time, Allan went to drill periodically and was off to summer camp every year learning the ABC of Army training under peaceful Canadian skies. The cheerful interest which the boy showed in all things helped him to learn quickly and well lessons which later served good purpose.

Besides having the usual hobbies and pastimes of a boy in a riverside town, Allan was a skilled wood-worker. From the making of book-ends, letter racks, and small tables, which a lad so often brings home to his mother from manual training and carpentry classes, Allan went on to the building of cupboards, cabinets, and similar pieces. So the busy carefree years passed.

In 1939, Allan was Regimental Sergeant-Major with the Highlanders. War was declared on Germany. The Regiment was plunged immediately into training for active service. Piper threw himself whole-heartedly into these activities and soon was commissioned as an officer. When the Stormont, Dundas, and Glengarry Highlanders went overseas, Lieutenant Allan Piper was one of their most efficient officers.

Soon, with thousands of other Canadians, Allan was helping to hold the front line that was the little island of Great Britain. There was not much of the high excitement of battle to key a man up to his best. There was no glorious rallying cry, nor clash of arms with an enemy met on firm ground. Instead, there was the grim waiting, waiting for one knew not what. There was plenty of hard work, and drill, drill, drill. And soon there was danger. For the roar of enemy planes shattered British skies. Death and destruction rained from the air, on soldiers and civilians, British and Canadians, alike.

"Why don't we go over there and finish it?" men asked day after day.

"What are we waiting for?" was the constant question.

Allan Piper, like his comrades, wondered and waited impatiently for the day when they could go out to battle with the relentless enemy. Meantime, there was work to be done. There were lessons of modern warfare to be learned. There were raw Canadian recruits to be taught. Allan soon found his place in this work. His own thorough knowledge, together with his ability to teach others and to win friends, soon came to official notice. He became an infantry training instructor.

The years 1940 and 1941 were terrible ones for England and, indeed, for all the world. Early in 1942 it seemed that Allied troops must soon cross the English Channel to fight on European soil. Strange and secret moves were made by night. Queer, unheard-of exercises were carried out by day. Training went on and on.

July arrived, with its hot, sunny days. At a camp in Southern England, Allan was teaching a group of men how to use the deadly missiles called hand-grenades. Again and again he had explained how, once the safety catch, or pin, is removed, the grenade must explode in a matter of seconds.

"Never pull the pin until ready to throw the grenade. Then be sure to toss it the moment the order is given. Don't get excited. Nothing can happen until you want it to," the young Lieutenant would say.

At first, the groups practised with "dummy" grenades. Then, as they became more skilled and sure, they were supplied with real ones, called "live" weapons. This was to show them exactly what to expect in battle. In this way, they became used to the shock of explosion, and so would not fall into confusion when quick thinking might mean the difference between life and death, victory and defeat.

On this fateful day of 27 July, 1942, Allan was with his group in the instruction pit. Here, well away from buildings, sheltered by the ground, the live grenades could be thrown without fear of damage. Again the Lieutenant had warned his men not to rush at it: to wait for orders, then obey instantly.

"And don't get excited, fellows," he cautioned, with his friendly encouraging smile.

The next few minutes were tense. Orders were given briskly. The pins were released. The dangerous missiles were tossed.

All seemed in order—then, suddenly, it was not. One nervous young man had fumbled his deadly handful. He clutched at it in panic but it rolled from his grasp. His hands closed on air. The grenade, on the point of explosion, thudded heavily to the ground, right in the midst of the little company.

The men stood as if frozen to the spot. Each one knew too well how quickly his life might be ticking away. A second passed. All at once, the Lieutenant leaped into action. He, too, knew, even better perhaps than his men, that death was about to strike in the pit. Yet he plunged forward, reaching out with both hands for the grenade.

He grasped its iron surface, but the time was up. With a blinding flash, the bomb exploded in his hands. Lieutenant Allan Piper "whom shape of danger could not dismay" had passed the highest test of bravery.

His act had saved the lives of several men. Now was to come the yet sterner, ultimate test of courage.

When Allan woke up in hospital some time afterwards, he woke to pain, and to darkness. For both his hands had been shattered by the bursting grenade, and he was blind. The days that followed were black indeed. There was no light in the young Lieutenant's eyes and little in his heart. Yet he asked no questions. He made no wild demands, as most men might do when facing a future without hands and without sight. He knew that skilful surgeons had amputated his mangled hands. He knew, too, that all their skill was centred upon giving him back his sight. So,

. . . he plunged forward, reaching out with both hands for the grenade.

lying there far away from his home and family, he faced his tragic problem squarely.

He thought about the loss of his hands and of what could be done in a work-a-day world without them. After a while, he felt that much could be done with the use of artificial limbs. But to be blind, as well, seemed, even to Allan Piper, almost too much to bear.

After six weeks of dreadful anxiety, there came for the young Canadian officer one of the most eventful days of his life. For on that day the bandages were taken from his eyes. As the doctor lifted the last bit of gauze from the right eye, he bent closer and looked carefully into Allan's face. Allan scarcely dared to breath. Presently the doctor straightened up, smiled a little, and said,

"Well, it looks as if this one is going to be O.K."

Those were quite the most welcome words Allan Piper had ever heard. And when the left eye, too, was found to be "O.K." he was truly happy.

The days that followed were cheerful ones. Allan's gay smile and friendliness made the other patients feel like cheering him on. One day they thought of a way to fix up a set of leather straps which could be useful to him in many ways. After much planning, they set to work. It wasn't long before a cleverly devised arrangement was fastened to Allan's shoulders. Day by day, he practised using this arrangement to do many things formerly done with his hands. Before long, he was trying to write. At the end of two months of painstaking effort, Allan wrote a letter home to his wife.

"It looks as if a fly had crawled out of the ink bottle and across the paper," he laughed, as he looked at the finished effort. "But at least it is the first step."

One day an important visitor came to the hospital. It was Lieutenant-General Montague, who was then Chief of Staff at Canadian Military Headquarters in London. After a little conversation, Allan said he would like to ask a question. The General was quite willing to hear it, of course, and, almost fearfully, Allan said:

"Well, sir—is there any possible chance of my staying in the Army?"

What a surprising question! Such a thing was unheard of—a man with no hands in a wartime Army! Yet, this man had something to offer. He had determination, intelligence—and courage. And the Army today has many uses for men besides actual fighting. There is, for instance, much office work; there is also the instructing of men in drill and discipline; there is an example to be set.

Even more surprising was the answer to Allan's question. The General said that the Army was well pleased with Lieutenant Piper, and that if he could just learn to write properly, his request would be granted. The second, and better written, letter was to General Montague. Lieutenant Allan Piper stayed in the Army.

Some months later, he was sent to another hospital to be fitted with artificial hands and taught to use them. The course of training here was supposed to last a month. After five days, Allan was discharged. He could eat, shave, clean his teeth—and write.

On 8 December, 1942 Lieutenant Piper returned to Canada. Early next year, he was posted to Barriefield Camp as Captain of a training company. Once again, he was a Canadian Army officer on duty. Until the war ended, Captain Piper carried on efficiently with his brother officers.

When the Second World War ended, Allan Piper returned, as did other Canadians, to civilian life, but not to the life he had known. He had to learn to fill a new place in a new way which demanded a different and perhaps even more tenacious courage.

After many difficult weeks, not one gap remained in his ordinary life, from the necessary acts of every day, to such skills as bowling, car-driving, even his old hobby of wood-working.

In time he was able to teach others similarly handicapped to live full and useful lives—following the lead of this one 'happy warrior', "persevering... from well to better".

WHERE ARE NOW YOUR PROPHETS? VII

"During the Session of 1937 I quoted Jeremiah . . . 'Where are now your prophets that prophesied unto you saying that the King of Babylon would not come against you, nor against this land?' Now we see what has happened in the St. Lawrence."

T. L. Church, M.P.
(Broadview)
House of Commons,
March 10, 1943.

THE AUTUMN night was still and cold with a light sea running, when the Newfoundland Government ferry *S.S. Caribou* left Sydney, Nova Scotia, on her overnight trip across Cabot Strait to Port-aux-Basques, Newfoundland.

Captain Benjamin Taverner, Master of the 17-year old vessel, was on the bridge scanning the dark water for the upthrust periscope of an enemy submarine. Below deck most of his nearly two hundred passengers had settled to sleep as arrival at Port-aux-Basques was due shortly after day-light.

It was an ordinary routine passage and those on board other than the forty-six crew members, were personnel of Canadian and American Armed Forces, as well as civilians, men, women and children.

Of the Canadian services were two Nursing Sisters of the Royal Canadian Navy, Nursing Dietitian Margaret

Brooke and her companion, Nursing Sister Agnes Wilkie. Both girls were from the Canadian inland provinces, Miss Brooke listing Ardath, Saskatchewan as home, and Miss Wilkie of Carmen, Manitoba.

Doubtless the two nurses were aware of what most civilian Canadians had not realized—the very real danger that lurked in the coastal waters off Canada's eastern limits. Yet, with the fortitude of their nature and calling, they slept as the little ferry ploughed on.

For 'Captain Ben' however, there was no relaxing of vigilance. Too many 'unsolved' disasters had occurred in these, his home waters, since the beginning of the Second World War, to be called accidental. And who knew how much earlier the crafty Nazi planning had plotted the path for their U-boats right to the very soil of our 'safe' Canada? Naturally it would have served no useful purpose to feed the already over-fevered and apprehensive imagination of the civilian population. That way lay panic, which panic, besides its obvious ill effects on morale, would certainly lower the desperately needed war effort of every man, woman and child.

So those who knew kept the secret, brooding on it often in the dark watches of the night as, perhaps, Captain Taverner brooded this night of 14 October, 1942.

As early as 1937, and even earlier, heads of state at home and abroad listened to the fanatical outpourings of Adolf Hitler. As they watched anxiously, his mesmerized hordes moved inexorably step by step to fulfill his mad but incredibly well-plotted dream of world domination. Mr. T. L. Church, Member of the Canadian House of Commons for Broadview, voiced fears and asked questions of the government. Mr. Church had reminded the House, of the fact that even then Germany had submarines capable of crossing the Atlantic without refueling.

"Are we to wait until the enemy comes up the St. Lawrence?" Mr. Church asked earnestly and repeatedly. Then, on March 10, 1943, he thundered his own reply to the hitherto unanswered questions in pre-war sessions.

"Where are now your prophets?"

For by that time the insidious war of the undersea attackers had come, not only to our gates, but on to the very earth of North America's oldest settlement, the "Fortress Isle" of Newfoundland and even up the water-highway of Canada's life-line, the St. Lawrence River.

It was, however, unlikely that Captain Ben was dwelling on the Canadian Parliament this dark night. It is doubtful if he had heard the declaration of German Grand Admiral Karl Donitz at the beginning of this year of 1942;

"The whole American coast is now open for operations by U-boats."

Yet the Master of the *Caribou,* plying this routine trip in familiar home waters, now become so threatening, knew the danger that lurked there. Had there not been unexplained disasters along the Coast, in the Gulf and certainly around the islands of St. Pierre and Miquelon?

Captain Taverner kept watch.

Perhaps the captain thought too, and tried to dismiss as rumour, the repeated tales of Nazi U-boat crewmen disguised as fishermen, who came ashore to drink in the taverns and bars of St. John's.

All this and more may have darkened the night watch of Captain Taverner and his officers.

Alertness was their creed but these times demanded constant vigilance. So the sturdy little *Caribou* steamed on to within less than thirty miles of her home port while passengers slept.

Suddenly a terrific shock struck the ferry, shuddering through the staterooms, throwing passengers from their bunks. As they ran to the decks in night clothes, water was already pouring into the ship from all sides.

Margaret Brooke was stunned for a few minutes by the crash. Yet while her body was momentarily helpless, her mind realized what must have happened. They had been torpedoed—almost in sight of shore. She and her Nursing Sister companion, with others of the service personnel, had not got to the War. The War had come to them.

As she shook off the effects of the shock, Margaret realized that Agnes was urging her to the lifeboat on the port side. The two girls staggered and rolled with the plunging of the stricken ship. But the lifeboat had been blasted away.

Life belts were the only hope, Margaret realized, and snatched at them as scalding steam gushed from the engine room. Deftly fastening the life belt around her, she saw Agnes was in trouble and could not cope with the safety device. Margaret pulled the shivering girl to her and fastened her snugly into the belt. By that time, in less than five minutes, the gallant little *Caribou* was settling on her way to the bottom of the Strait.

The two girls were tossed into the cold churning water, while the *Caribou* plunged down, bow first, carrying her gallant Captain, his two ship's Officer-sons and all but about a dozen of his crew.

Survivors related that the Master of the doomed *Caribou,* in a last ditch attempt to destroy the destroyer, steered the sinking vessel directly at the now surfaced U-boat. But the *Caribou* slid under the waves before her ice-breaker prow could ram the Nazi submarine. And a great suction pulled and flung the survivors struggling in the cold water.

All this happened in a matter of minutes in the darkest hour of pre-dawn. The torpedo struck at 2:40 a.m. Atlantic Standard Time. Passengers clung to flotsam, found rafts of debris, and some crowded into the remaining intact lifeboats. As the U-boat surfaced, she capsized several of the frail rafts and her hull smashed into a lifeboat.

Meanwhile, the two Naval Nursing Sisters floundered in the surging waves. An overturned lifeboat floated within reach.

"Come on, Agnes, we can hang on here and wait for rescue," Margaret gasped.

But already Agnes was weakening. Margaret hauled her within grasp of the slippery craft. By this time, about a dozen others were clinging to the rough ropes on the boat and striving desperately to get a hold on the up-turned vessel.

Minutes dragged into hours. The sea roughened as daylight approached and the plight of the ill-clad people was terrible. Waves slapped at and curled over the overturned lifeboat. One by one the freezing survivors were washed off.

Nursing Sister Brooke anxiously watched her comrade and tried to bolster Agnes' visibly sinking strength.

"The rescue boats are coming, Agnes", she cried. "It won't be long. Hang on."

But Agnes began to slip, her hold weakening rapidly. Margaret wriggled her own numb body closer to Agnes, tightened one hand's hold on the rope and grabbed at her friend with the other. She was just in time, as Agnes had developed cramp forcing her to let go.

Naval rescue craft on patrol were steaming to the scene, among them *H.M.C.S. Grandmere*. The first grey streaks of dawn lightened the eastern sky. Still Margaret Brooke held her almost helpless companion. Her own strength was failing and her arms trembled and ached with the double strain. Still she clung desperately to life, and the life of her friend.

With the rising sea waves roughened and washed over the capsized vessel. Just as day came a huge breaker swept the two nursing sisters apart. Emerging weakly from the onslaught, one arm almost frozen to the rope, Margaret looked for Agnes. She called her name but no answer came back.

Searching the rocking waves, Margaret thought she glimpsed the other girl being washed away.

Willing her almost unconscious body, she made an effort to reach Agnes, but all her attempts failed and no sound came from the engulfing water.

Margaret Brooke was not able to tell how she was finally rescued. She knew only that after Agnes had drowned, she, herself, sank into numb oblivion. Later she was told that a sailor had dived into the water, loosened her desperate grasp on the life boat, and took her aboard the rescue ship.

The toll was heavy in that attack in home waters. Of 237 lives, 136 were lost.

In his statement following the disaster, Canadian Navy Minister Macdonald said, "It brings the War to Canada with tragic emphasis."

Of Nursing Sister Agnes Wilkie, the Minister said, "She was the first of our Nursing Sisters to lose her life in this War and she died, in truth, in action. The Navy and Naval Nursing Service will treasure this young woman's memory."

Of Nursing Sister Margaret Martha Brooke, R.C.N., the nation, on 1 January, 1942, declared her to be a Member of the Military Division of the Most Excellent Order of the British Empire, *"For gallantry and courage.* After the sinking of the Newfoundland ferry, *S.S. Caribou,* this officer displayed great courage while in the water in attempting to save the life of another Nursing Sister."

And in June of that same year, the Right Honourable W. L. MacKenzie King, Prime Minister of Canada, made a statement in the House of Commons, "with respect to measures which have been adopted . . . in the organization of the lower St. Lawrence region, with a view more particularly to countering expected submarine activities in that area".

So the gallantry and loss on that cold October night, was not wasted. As Sir Winston Churchill had said of the Dieppe raid a few months earlier, equally applicable to the thousands of lives lost subsequently in battle action,

> " . . . Honour to the brave who fell,
> their sacrifice was not in vain."

IT WAS MY JOB

VIII

WELL, its a job, anyway," said young Fred Topham as he packed his belongings at his home in Toronto. He and his brother, Bob, were off to Northern Ontario to work in a big gold mine there. Fred, or "Toppy" as his chums called him, was not long out of high school and jobs were scarce in Toronto then. Anyhow, in his quiet way, Toppy looked forward to playing even a small part in the romantic search for gold.

His boyish ideas of romance and adventure, however, did not prove entirely true to fact. The work in the big Kirkland Lake mine was hard and sometimes, perhaps, dangerous. But the lad did not turn away from it on that account. Instead, he gave the strength of his tall, young body to the work at hand, building firm muscles that were later to serve him well.

When, late in 1939, young Canadians were being called to military service across the seas, Toppy returned to Toronto to enlist. He chose a certain regiment and applied for a place in it. But the regiment already had its required number of men. Heavy demands upon manpower were being made by factories and industries doing important work, with many of their employees gone to war. Not being required for the Service he had selected, Toppy decided to fill a vacancy in one of these industries. So for two years he worked in a factory, on the alert to find some department of the Army to which he could give his best service.

Finally, on 3 August, 1942, he once again presented himself to the military authorities. He was accepted this time and went at once to a camp for basic training. At last he knew definitely where he wanted to play his part in the Army. This was with the fearless paratroops, whose men had to be entirely sound of body, mind, and spirit, and possessed of a high degree of daring. When Toppy asked for a transfer to this special Service, he had all these qualities—and more. Alas, he had too much! He weighed thirty pounds more than was allowed for these soldiers who must descend from the air by parachute.

Toppy had made up his mind, however. He accepted a course in signalling at Kingston, determined to lose those extra pounds in the shortest possible time. Accordingly, he set himself a course of training. He ate as little as possible, and every morning and every night he jogged long distances. Often he must have been hungry, for his big, healthy body needed large quantities of fuel, and his vigorous training must have sharpened his appetite. For ten exhausting days he followed this routine. He was beginning to feel weak from the short rations and long exercises. Yet he felt he had lost sufficient weight to try again for the paratroops.

He had no scales on which to weigh himself, so it was with uncertain hopes that he presented himself for another medical examination. This time he was successful. His weight was down to 175 pounds.

After intensive training in the United States, he sailed for England and action in July, 1943. Then began another period of training, which became harder and more dangerous as the days crept on towards the great Invasion of 1944. One day, an urgent request came to the 1st Canadian Parachute Battalion. It was for volunteers for the Medical Corps. Something in this call appealed to Fred Topham and before long he offered his services.

Then began still another course of training. He and

the others in the medical group learnt all kinds of difficult and exciting things. They were taken up in a plane and taught to jump, carrying medical supplies. Sometimes Toppy carried only his first-aid kit. Sometimes he leaped from the low-flying plane clasping a collapsible stretcher. There was one sort of burden he did not carry on these jumps, however—a weapon of any kind. For all who go into battle for any purpose other than that of killing the enemy must go unarmed. The only protection of the Medical Corps is the big Red Cross badge on sleeve or cap. This is to show the enemy that the wearer is on an errand of mercy and will try to save life rather than to destroy it. But the scarlet cross on the white background is not always seen, in the heat of battle.

As the spring days of 1944 drew quickly into summer, all sailors, and airmen were filled with a deeply eager excitement. They knew that very soon a great invasion was to be made on the continent of Europe to drive the enemy from his strongholds there. Most of them hoped they would be among the first to cross the Channel. Certainly, Corporal Fred Topham, medical orderly, hoped so. As the excitement rose, and soldiers guessed at the date (for only a very few high officers knew it), training was serious indeed.

At last that fateful 6 June, 1944, dawned. "D-Day" had come and great shiploads of soldiers sailed for France. But Toppy was not with them. He was in hospital suffering from some slight illness. His disappointment was great. Still, he was not long behind his friends. In August, he joined his battalion in France.

Although there was a great deal of bitter fighting throughout France, Belgium, and Holland all winter, Toppy's biggest day did not come until the next spring. On 24 March, 1945, the 1st Canadian Parachute Battalion was ordered to jump from the planes into a strongly defended enemy area, on the east side of the Rhine River, in Germany. Of course, Toppy went with the battalion. As the plane roared over Germany, the Commanding Officer talked quietly with his men. Every man waited tensely for the order to jump.

At last it came. The plane was flying about six hundred feet above the ground at this time. Toppy checked his parachute and walked in his turn to the door. He kept his thoughts on getting to the ground as quickly as possible. The air was thick with anti-aircraft fire, but he was not hit. Soon he bumped to earth, suffered no injury in the landing. When he had disentangled himself from parachute harness, he looked quickly about him. He saw at once that they had overshot their intended landing-place. They were directly in the open *behind* the enemy lines. The first command, in such a contingency, is to get back as quickly as possible to the intended landing-place. This, Toppy thought of doing. For two good reasons, however, he soon changed his mind. In the first place, he found that his little group was cut off from the rest of the battalion and surrounded by the enemy, so that return was difficult and every step fraught with danger. But the main reason was, for Toppy, the pitiful cries for help that began to reach his ears. All around him lay paratroopers badly injured in landing. So Toppy went to work.

The gun-fire blasted all around him. But he ignored it. First one wounded man was tended as well as possible, then another. Swiftly and calmly, Toppy worked on. When he had done his best for a casualty, he lifted him in his strong arms and carried him to whatever safety there might be. Hour after hour he carried on, working single-handed or with other members of the Medical Corps who happened to be nearby. Gradually, and with the utmost care, he worked his way back towards contact with the rest of his battalion.

About eleven o'clock, there came the sharp cry of a wounded man from an open space in clear view of the enemy. Two medical orderlies rushed out to his aid. They knelt beside him and began rapid treatment. Rat-tat-tat! There was a savage burst of fire right beside them.

. . . he lifted him in his strong arms, and carried him to whatever safety there might be.

Both orderlies toppled over, killed instantly. Yet the wounded man still lived.

Toppy, who had seen the tragedy, dashed out amid the heavy firing. The way seemed twice as long as it really was. Reaching the sufferer, Toppy dropped to his knees beside him and continued with the work started by the dead orderlies.

"Hang on, old man," he murmured comfortingly. "We'll soon get you out of this." Spang-gg! A bullet whined very close to Toppy's head.

"Enemy sniper," he thought. "Guess he's got my range, too." But his steady hands never paused in their work.

Next instant another bullet whizzed, even closer to his ears. And then Toppy felt a sudden stinging blow. Blood gushed from his nose. The sniper's aim had been true.

Still Toppy did not stop, for his task was not quite finished.

"There," he gasped through bloodstained lips, "that will do for now. Let's go!"

And bending all his superb strength to the task he lifted the wounded man in his arms. Slowly, steadily, he bore him across the open space into the shelter of the woods.

When he had safely delivered his burden, the Corporal applied meagre first aid to himself. He taped a dressing carelessly over his nose, and went out again into the open.

Soon, all the casualties had been taken to shelter. During a brief lull in the firing, someone noticed Toppy's bleeding nose.

"Hey, feller," several cried, "get yourself to the M.O. (Medical Officer) for treatment."

Eventually, the pain and discomfort forced Toppy to decide to do just this. Upon being given treatment at the first-aid post, he was immediately ordered to return back of the lines to hospital. Toppy begged permission to stay on duty.

"After all, sir, I'd like to see the finish after being in this long," he pleaded.

His determination, added to the valuable service he could give, won his point for him. With his nose so badly swollen that it felt, as he said afterwards, like a football, he set out to rejoin his company farther forward. On his way, he came upon a gun-carrier which had been hit by enemy fire. It was blazing fiercely and sharp bursts ripped from it at all angles as its own ammunition exploded. The three crew members were badly injured and still trapped inside.

Toppy did not hesitate. He plunged towards the burning machine. Someone shouted at him. An officer had warned everyone against trying to approach the carrier. It seemed to mean certain death to those who tried. Toppy paid little attention to the shouting. Three men needed help that he had been trained to give.

Like huge firecrackers on a festive holiday, the ammunition rocketed about the medical orderly. He hauled the nearest man free. Then he went back for the next. Finally, all three lay clear of the burning carrier.

The trip across open ground back to the first-aid post had to be made three times. And three times the fearless corporal made it. Willing helpers came out to meet him, and soon the suffering men were being eased of some of their pain. Although rescue came too late for one of the carrier crew, two of the three undoubtedly owed their lives to Toppy Topham. Yet they were but two of the many who had reason that day to bless his sure, strong hands and sturdy arms.

Back home in Canada, Corporal Frederick George Topham was told that he had been awarded the Victoria Cross. His first remark was in keeping with the "Toppy" his friends knew and liked so well—

"I only did what every man in my outfit would do. It was my job."

JUST LUCK

IX

THE TRAIN whistled sharply and began chugging in quickening rhythm. The wheels turned with increasing speed. And slowly the railway station at Kitchener, Ontario, slid past. From the dusty windows, dozens of brown boyish faces laughed and cheered noisily, calling boisterous good-byes to friends on the platform. Among the tanned faces was one with a particularly gay smile. Fairly brimming with health and high spirits, Rod Ball shouted messages and bits of nonsense to the chums he was leaving behind him in his home town. The occasion was one of Canada's harvest excursions to the Great West. The time was late in the 1920's. Rod Ball was just one of the many young Canadians who yearly yield to the lure of the romantic call, "Go West, young man". Where many find the hard work and the rigorous climate not quite to their liking, and so come east again, Rod was different. He had always been a great lover of the outdoors, and in the wide open spaces of Canada's West he found the freedom his young heart craved.

When he had served his turn with the Saskatchewan grain, he left the farm to seek a living in some more adventurous way.

Since the days when stealthy-footed Indians tracked down the fur-bearing animals of the Northwest, the lonely life of a trapper has always appealed to fearless, venturesome boys. Rod Ball was one of these.

It was not long, therefore, before Rod was following the rugged trails of the Northwest. During winter, he set his traps along some frozen river, or in some pathless forest. Many frosty dawns heard the swish of his snowshoes as he tramped from trap to trap to find his catches. The bitter cold of starry nights found him heading wearily back to his lonely cabin, there to build a roaring fire and prepare a hearty meal.

Springtime came and the young trapper loaded his canoe with the winter's catch of furs and headed down stormy, tumbling waters to the trading-posts. It was a hard, free life. Rod Ball revelled in it, as his body grew magnificently strong and his senses keen as an Indian's. Little could he foresee the future for which this early experience was hardening him. Yet he learned lessons in woodcraft and hunting lore never to be forgotten.

During the year 1929, Rod turned from the trails to seek some more secure means of making a living. Still yearning for the outdoor life, he felt drawn to the active and adventurous work of the Royal Canadian Mounted Police. He applied for entrance into the Force at Regina, Saskatchewan. On 4 November, 1929, he was accepted and signed on as a constable. Rod Ball became a "Mountie".

After finishing his early training, he was posted to the west coast. He was on duty at different stations there until 1931, when he got his first chance to go on patrol into the North. This was the beginning of many eventful patrols for Constable Ball.

In lonely places, where often the brilliant red coat of the Mountie is the only emblem of law and authority, Rod found much of the romance and excitement he wanted. Yet the stern discipline and the task of faithfully attending to humdrum routine duties drilled him in the qualities which were to stand him in such good stead in the exacting years to come. Month by month his body hardened to an endurance and strength far beyond the average. And the word "danger" meant only excitement to Rod Ball.

When war broke upon the world in 1939, Rod was eager to get into action with the Armed Forces. But first he must finish his appointed service with the R.C.M.P. This duty was fulfilled on 4 November, 1941, after twelve years with one of the most famous and colourful police forces in the world.

On the very next day, Rod joined the Royal Canadian Air Force. His big aim had been to become a fighter pilot. He was disappointed in this, however, because he was a little older than the age limit set down at that time for R.C.A.F. pilots. At first he did not know what to do.

"You may apply for and receive your discharge, and re-enlist with the Service Police, if you wish," he was told. "You would probably get an officer's commission in that Branch."

But the idea of rank did not appeal to the young man so much as the more exciting forms of duty.

"You may start in a training course for air-gunners, then," was the next offer.

Eagerly Rod accepted this chance. Soon, he was being taught all the details of this most hazardous occupation. Seven months later, he was in England.

At this time, gallant Allied airmen were making history in the danger-filled skies over Europe. Night and day, huge squadrons of aeroplanes roared out over the English Channel, to bomb enemy targets on the continent. Other airmen, in fighter planes, hunted the skies to meet and destroy the Nazi air marauders. It was with the former group, the huge bombers, that Rod pursued his duty. As rear gunner in a Halifax bomber, he sought a prey far more dangerous than the four-footed creatures of his early trapping days. He pursued enemies far more cruel than the evil-doers of his police years.

Time after time, he had narrow escapes with his comrades. Mission after mission was completed without mishap in the war-blasted skies. But, at last, the almost inevitable crash came. On 19 June, 1943, Rod and his comrades were over France about one o'clock in the morning.

The aircraft, on its way home from a night bombing raid, was flying fairly low, just over the city of Caen, a bit inland from the Channel.

Suddenly, the red-orange burst of flak (anti-aircraft fire) began exploding all around them. Before the pilot could take any evasive action at all, a shattering blow struck one wing. The shuddering aircraft spun and whirled, down, down, plunging heavily towards the swift-approaching earth. Just a half mile from where it was hit, the bomber crashed and ploughed upside down into the ground. The terrific speed and force of the crash splintered it to pieces.

It would seem that no one could possibly escape from such wreckage. Yet Rod, caged in his glass turret, did just that. Thrown by the tremendous jolt, the turret rolled completely free from the smashed and bursting body of the plane. After the first shock, the gunner gained enough strength to make his way out of the turret. Badly shaken, and cut and bruised from head to foot, he forced himself to crawl free. He found himself in a field of tall golden wheat. There, not far from him, lay the wreck of his plane. One engine had burst into flames, but the body was not yet burning. Rod climbed painfully to his feet, intending to struggle towards the plane and seek his comrades. He took a step, but instantly one leg gave way beneath him. He fell to the ground, conscious only of sharp pain. He knew that his leg was broken. As he tried to crawl, dragging the injured leg, he rolled sideways. One of his arms was useless, probably broken, too. Nevertheless, he crawled on.

Reaching the burning plane, he peered anxiously through a gaping hole in its side. One glance showed him that the three crew members, lying there, were beyond his help. Rod was exausted and in great pain. Still he turned away to seek some of the other crew members. As he did so, he heard a low moan. Following the sound, he came upon the pilot, jammed into the fuselage and terribly wounded.

Exerting his mighty powers of endurance, Rod forgot his own injuries and worked frantically to release his comrade. Finally, he had him free.

As he huddled over the suffering man on the ground, the gunner had to work by touch rather than sight in the dark. He felt the great wound in his friend's head. Sick with his own pain, and with pity for the other man, he fumbled with his handkerchief and managed to tie on a clumsy sort of bandage. He was just finishing the delicate job, when approaching footsteps and rough voices startled him. A bright torch was flashed into his face. The enemy was upon him. R.C.M.P. ex-Constable Ball was a prisoner-of-war.

Roughly the Germans examined his wounds and made a rude sort of splint for his broken leg so that he could use it. His other injuries they did not touch. In the dim light, Rod watched them roll the unconscious pilot onto a broken door and carry him away. The captors then took their one remaining prisoner to a nearby village and locked him up in the huge old-fashioned stone gaol there.

After a sleepless night, Rod was taken by truck to Paris, where he was held for two days waiting for a train. He was given no medical attention there. Only his rugged stamina made those long hours bearable. The next move was to a prison hospital where wounded airmen were held for questioning. Here the overworked, hurried medical staff gave his injuries some slight care. After being questioned and giving no answers, Rod was moved again to a prison called Stalag Luft III. Here, half-way between the two German cities of Berlin and Breslau, nearly ten thousand British, Canadian and American airmen were imprisoned. The prison was made up of three camps, separated from each other by dense forest. Rod was taken to the middle one. Here he remained for some months. Then he was moved to the North Camp. It was here that he faced still another and perhaps his greatest adventure.

North Camp lay in the centre of an area where tall pine

trees had grown many, many years earlier. The ground in this compound was still thickly dotted with great tree stumps. These the prisoners were supposed to cut out, and then they were allowed to use them for firewood in their huts. Two high barbed-wire fences, seven feet apart, surrounded the prison yard. In the seven-foot space between the fences great rolls of barbed-wire were packed. Forty feet inside the fences was a safety wire. One step past this wire called down the fire from the many guard towers around the yard. These towers were fifteen feet high and held, besides the guard, a great searchlight and a machine-gun. Beyond the grim fences stretched the thick, dark forests. The underbrush had been cut, leaving few hiding places near the camp.

Escape from such a stronghold would seem hopeless. Yet hundreds of the prisoners in North Camp, Stalag Luft III, hoped—and dared. When Rod arrived at North Camp, plans for such an attempt were well organized and under way. Rod lost no time in volunteering for the attempt. He was readily accepted and took his place with the other fearless workers.

The idea was to dig a tunnel—under the hut, under the prison yard, under the very guard towers—which would emerge into the shadowy depths of the forest. Each man was given the task best suited to him. Civil engineers planned the tunnel, miners delved and dug, tailors gathered pieces of cloth to make civilian clothing. Identification papers were forged and maps traced. Even those who had no special skill played important parts. For instance, getting rid of the earth and sand removed from the tunnel had been a problem. This was solved by sewing long sacks inside the trousers of a large number of the prisoners. These sacks were filled with the sand and fitted with draw-strings. The carriers then wandered off to join different groups, watching soft-ball or volley-ball games. The watchers crowded close about them. Carefully, the carriers released their loads, moving about in the thickest part of the crowd. Dozens of shuffling feet soon stamped the spilled earth well into the ground, and the carriers returned with empty sacks ready for the next loading.

So the work went on and on, month after weary month. The constant dread of horrible punishment, which would surely come with discovery, cannot be pictured in words. The aching of muscles and the exhaustion of under-nourished bodies cannot be imagined. Only the men engaged in this high bid for freedom could really know what these things meant. Yet finally, at the beginning of the second week in March, 1944, the tunnel measured 240 feet. On the twelfth day of the month, the diggers bored upwards until they came to tree roots. They built make-shift ladders into the sides of the shaft, and two days later all was ready for the great attempt.

Although nearly six hundred men had worked on the project, only about two hundred could hope to get through in one night. About fifty of the leaders were to go first; twenty others were chosen by secret ballot; and another one hundred and forty names were drawn from a hat. Rod Ball's name was among these last.

The night of March 24 was dark and windy. There was no moon and at first conditions promised to be ideal for the attempt at escape. Each man had been supplied with a map showing the particular route he was to take. Tense with excitement, they waited to start at the appointed hour. Then came the first stroke of bad luck.

Snow began to fall thickly, covering the ground with a white blanket. How clearly and dangerously footprints would show on that pure surface! Nevertheless, the die was cast. They must go on.

Finally, the signal to start was given. One by one, the men worked their way down into the earth. Progress was slow, but at length the first man pushed his way up through the bit of earth covering the opening at the end of the tunnel. Quickly he drew back again. "What could be wrong?" thought the men waiting tensely behind him. They soon found out. In spite of all precautions, the tunnel was short of its goal. Instead of being hidden by the

Not fifteen yards from the gaping hole, the grim outline of a guard tower loomed darkly against the sky.

woods, the outlet of the shaft was ten feet this side of the first forest trees. Not fifteen yards from the gaping hole, the grim outline of a guard tower loomed darkly against the sky.

It was too late to turn back. Waiting only to get a second breath, the leader climbed out and wriggled towards the fringe of the forest. He let out a rope behind him with which to signal to the second man when to start. In just an hour, the first twenty men stood in the friendly shadow of the trees. They formed lines like a military company, marking time, then marched quickly and boldly away. In this way, the sound of their tramping feet could easily be mistaken for the changing of the guard. After going several yards deeper into the forest, the prisoners separated and struck off in different directions.

Hour after hour, the same pattern was followed. Groups of tens and twenties lined up and marched off into the forest. Altogether, eighty-three prisoners climbed from the tunnel and escaped into the woods before a guard came upon its yawning mouth. Immediately a great alarm was raised. Telephone wires buzzed with warnings; radio sets tapped out the news. Orders were sent back and forth. Storm-troopers, Gestapo, Nazi soldiers, sailors, airmen, and even Hitler Youth Groups were turned loose in the hunt. The German countryside was alive with thousands of watchful eyes.

Meantime, Rod's course led him straight through the woods. No one overtook him during the night, and by morning he had travelled quite a distance from camp. Not for nothing had he tramped the winding trails of Canada's West and North. His years of tracking down fugitives as a red-coated Mountie had taught him many of the tricks of flight. Yet all his skill could not serve to hide his tracks in the soft snow when daylight came. Before the sun was high in the sky, his Nazi pursuers had overtaken him. In a short time, he was back in Stalag Luft III.

Several days passed before the disappointed airmen

learned the full outcome of the brave attempt. Only three made good their escape. Others, who, like Rod Ball, were taken by local guards, returned to Stalag Luft III. But fifty of the eighty-three were not so lucky. They were captured by the Gestapo and taken to another camp at Gorlitz. A few days later the Commandant of the Camp at Stalag Luft III made a horrifying announcement. The men taken by the Gestapo had been shot at Gorlitz.

Rod Ball was present when the badly shaken survivors joined with their camp fellows in a memorial service for their executed comrades. It was a sad and solemn occasion, but there was high honour for the fallen.

Few men could survive so many hardships, with such a terrible ending, and still learn to smile again. Rod Ball is one of the few. Perhaps today if someone should say to him, "How did you do it?" he might answer with his old-time smile as he used to say of his successful patrols in the Force: "Just luck, that's all. Just luck."

Yet those who hear of fine record must surely say, "Not luck—but pluck indeed."

THE TRUE GLORY

X

> "O Lord God, when Thou givest to Thy servants to endeavour any great matter, grant us also to know that it is not the beginning but the continuing of the same, until it is thoroughly finished, which yieldeth the true glory, through Him that for the finishing of Thy work laid down His life, Our Redeemer Jesus Christ."
>
> —Drake's Prayer on Sailing into Cadiz

THE TELEPHONE rang insistently in the Toronto office of Captain Fred Slocombe, Master Mariner. A cold gleam of January sunshine fell across the desk from which the Captain lifted the receiver.

"Slocombe here."

"Captain Fred Slocombe? Ottawa calling, sir. Just a moment, please," came the clear tones of the operator. Then a quietly authoritative voice spoke in greeting over the wires from the Dominion's capital city.

"About this icebreaker for North Russia—will you take her there?"

The Captain's heart seemed to skip a beat, and a tumult of disturbing thoughts rushed into his mind. In the next few moments he asked and answered routine questions, but all the while his brain was in a whirl.

For this was the beginning of the year 1942, and the shadows of war hung darkly over the world. In far-off

Russia, stalwart troops battled across vast snowy wastes, through ice-clad cities, to stay the Nazi hordes bent upon conquest. And through the stormy northern waters within the Arctic Circle, convoys of United Nations ships plied their dangerous ways, carrying supplies to the Russian Allies. These ships were manned by Merchant Seamen—daring, venturesome sailors who accepted hardship and peril on the ocean as their daily lot. Even in the quiet times of peace the sea has its dangers. In days of war these are still present, and to them are added the risks of enemy attack; attack that may come from surface craft, from submarines ranging beneath the waves, from the skies.

Men of the Merchant Navy were not bound under oath to serve "for the duration". Theirs was not the iron discipline of military service. Recommended only by their waterproofed record books, which they carried from one ship's master to another, they voluntarily signed on to perform gruelling and wearisome duties on board ship, going "there and back". Often they did not come back. Yet those who did turned again, after brief rest ashore, to the rolling seas, so that the "life-line" to besieged Europe might hold.

It was men such as these that Captain Fred Slocombe, himself a seaman since the age of fifteen, was called upon to command on that Friday afternoon in late January, 1942. The Canadian Government had presented, along with other equipment, the icebreaker *Montcalm* to the Russian Government. The *Montcalm* had to be taken to Russia and handed over to the authorities by Canadian seamen. It was this task which was so quietly and abruptly assigned to Captain Slocombe. And the Master Mariner knew that he would accept it just as quietly. The tradition of the sea was in him; he would not question the decision of his Chief in Ottawa.

And yet he had no wish to go to North Russia. He had been some time ashore, away from actual seafaring. From early boyhood until shortly before the outbreak of war, he had served on ships travelling the waterways of the world. He had just begun to enjoy a settled and happy home life; since 1937 he had been Supervising Examiner of Masters and Mates with the Government Department of Transport. When Canada entered the war he immediately offered his services for sea duty, but was told he could not be spared from his important post. Yet now, more than two years later, his offer was suddenly accepted. At last he was urgently needed. So, worried and quite unprepared, Captain Fred Slocombe left the happy comfort of his home that very night, to get ready for the cold and hazardous route to northern Russia.

Three days later the Captain was hurrying through the murky streets of wartime Halifax, then so carefully called "an East Coast Canadian port". From ship to Customs Office, from Mercantile Marine Office to Naval Office he went, making the thousand arrangements necessary for a wartime voyage in midwinter.

In the comparative calm of Bedford Basin, drab vessels of all shapes and sizes slipped quietly into their positions in long columns. Ships carrying foodstuffs, ships carrying clothing, ships carrying ammunition, ships heavily freighted with aviation oil, and in the midst the little Canadian icebreaker, fresh from her duty on the peaceful St. Lawrence—all headed into the enemy-infested seas.

The skies were grey and sullen. The sea was rough and flecked with foam. A chill mist settled over the rows of rolling ships with their galaxy of Allied flags. Captain Slocombe, feeling again the roll of the deck beneath him, thrilled with pride and excitement as he watched the Canadian ensign fluttering at the stern of the little *Montcalm*. Resolutely he put aside all memories of Toronto and the happiness of his home.

The Commodore, from his ship somewhere in the centre front of the convoy, gave orders by means of flag signals. Radio silence had to be preserved except in case of extreme emergency. It was necessary then for the officers on the bridge of each ship to keep on the watch at all times for these signals. The close formation of the ships in the convoy posed the constant threat of collision.

This was Captain Slocombe's first experience of convoy duty. But as he peered into the ominous darkness of those first cold January nights, when no ships might show a light, he realized that within a stone's throw of him, another shadowy craft glided along. Its hold might be loaded with explosive. The slightest bump in this gloom could swiftly bring death to the crews of both ships; could jeopardize the entire convoy. Unremitting vigilance, then, was the price of safety. Yet even this was no guarantee against prowling U-boats, nor against the menace of German aircraft.

One by one, however, the dull cold days passed. Although occasionally the icebreaker shuddered violently from the concussion of depth charges, reminding all hands that submarines might strike at any moment, no full-scale enemy action was encountered. The signal flags, whipping up from time to time on the Commodore's ship and relayed from every vessel in the convoy, brought only routine messages.

At length, one day, aircraft were heard circling in the clouds above. All eyes watched the flagship anxiously. But the Commodore signalled that the planes were friendly; and soon the convoy was escorted into harbour in Scotland. The first stage of the voyage had been accomplished, not without discomfort and alarms, but certainly in safety. What might happen during the next stage no one could say, and few cared to think.

After nearly three weeks in Scotland, grappling with problems of still more detailed preparation and organization, Captain Slocombe again piloted the *Montcalm* out to sea. While the wind freshened over the choppy waters, he recalled the eventful Conference Day at the Naval Control Offices in Scotland. There, with as many as five other skippers, he had received instructions and information given briefly and frankly.

"You will be under attack by air, and quite possibly by

surface craft, too. But you will have with you a couple of heavy cruisers, as well as your lighter escort ships," they were told.

Again, the Control Officer had warned them tersely: "It is quite likely you will be attacked by four enemy destroyers known to be in the vicinity, perhaps even the *Scharnhorst* may get out at you. Against that, you have two heavy cruisers, your destroyers, anti-aircraft ships and submarines. You will doubtless be able to take care of yourselves if you keep your eyes open and obey orders at all times."

Vigilance and obedience were the watchwords as the convoy steamed from Iceland to the harbour of Murmansk in north Russia. They were now well above the Arctic Circle. The sky was heavy with leaden snow-laden clouds. The sea was an icy, slate-coloured, heaving mass. And within easy striking distance were the German planes based in Norway.

The first few days out an Allied air escort flew overhead, but now, whenever aircraft engines were heard in the distance, the Captain of the *Montcalm* and all his fellow-skippers looked apprehensively towards the flagship for a warning signal. For quite a long time their anxiety seemed unwarranted. Then, suddenly, came an alert. The sombre colours of the flags spelled out,

"Attack by aircraft must be expected".

Grimly the Captain gave his orders. There was a hustle of orderly excitement through the ship. The men carried out each order with skill and promptness.

The skipper's eyes strained towards the flagship. Again the flags changed.

"Enemy aircraft are approaching the convoy".

It was ten o'clock in the evening when the first attack came.

"We're for it all right!" exclaimed Captain Slocombe.

Out of the clouds two great bombers, Junkers 88's, headed straight towards the centre of the convoy. The gun crews immediately went into action. From every available gun, from every ship, anti-aircraft fire spouted upwards; the sky was like a fiery grid. The two bombers swerved erratically. From his place on the bridge, the Captain saw one of them dip uncertainly, right itself for a moment; then it lurched drunkenly, jettisoned its bombs, and plunged into the sea. The other, routed by the blazing greeting, gained altitude and slid rapidly out of sight.

Some of the tension passed from the men.

"That's the stuff to give them, boys. I guess we *can* look after ourselves, at that," the Captain congratulated them. He turned to look out across the convoy, scanning the ships for signs of damage. All at once he caught sight of the two heavy cruisers in the centre. They appeared to be putting on speed. He spoke to one of his officers near him.

"What are they doing over there, I wonder?"

Then he shifted his gaze to the Commodore's ship. Had he possibly missed a signal to put on speed? No, the other ships were maintaining the same pace as before. He turned again to the cruisers now slipping swiftly ahead between the long lines of plodding merchant vessels. A signal flag fluttered from their halyards.

"Well, of all things! 'Good Luck,' they say. Looks as though they're leaving us to it. Surely we didn't do *that* well," ejaculated the Captain in surprise and some dismay, with a little of his confidence ebbing away. It was not until later, however, that he heard about the distress signal received from another British warship which had been under attack by four enemy destroyers beyond the horizon. The cruisers were speeding to give what aid they could to the sinking vessel.

Meantime the long cold night drew on without further alarms. Not for a moment, nevertheless, were the Captain and his officers off guard. Never did the crew relax at their posts. Just about an hour's flight away, many enemy planes were based. The convoy was a slow one, for it had of necessity to proceed only as fast as the slowest ship. There was plenty of time for the routed enemy to return to base, pick up another load of bombs, and, perhaps reinforced by other aircraft, return to the attack. The numbing chill of the Arctic crept into the seamen's weary bones. Cups of hot tea and coffee, gulped between duties and watches, were not enough to resist it.

Morning came and wore into noonday. Early in the afternoon three specks were observed low over the horizon.

The alarm bells sounded "Action Stations" throughout the convoy. The three enemy planes circled their target again and again, like huge birds of prey waiting to spy out a weakness below. They kept warily out of range of the ships' guns, never attacking, ever threatening.

The Captain gave the order to don shrapnel helmets, and to see that life-belts were handy.

"Looks as though Jerry's carrying on a little war of nerves. He probably won't attack for hours," speculated the Captain. Yet he knew and every man knew, that they dare not lose sight of those wheeling, menacing specks, lest they suddenly close in. There was little to do, except to remain on the alert and wait in grim suspense.

Nine ominous hours dragged by. In the murky Arctic dusk of one o'clock in the morning, it was no longer possible to make out the dark line of the horizon. But the warning signal was still up. The hovering enemy planes still shadowed the crawling columns of ships.

Suddenly there was a hoarse shout aboard the *Montcalm*. Peering through the gloom, the Captain saw three planes coming in over the starboard bow. As they roared over the leading ships they were flying incredibly low.

On they came with nothing now between them and the little *Montcalm*; at least one of them singled her out. Every gun that the crew of the icebreaker could muster was blazing away at the oncoming aircraft. The very air seemed to crumble. The agony of the bitter cold was forgotten in the confusion of battle. Tracer bullets slashed the Arctic twilight with curving blades of light. And it seemed to Captain Slocombe that the desperate fire from his little vessel was having some effect. Just before reaching the *Montcalm*, the attacking plane banked sharply and flew across the bows. The guns on the foredeck broke into renewed uproar. As the plane flew ahead of the ship, the Captain saw tracer bullets streaking into the fuselage. A red glare of flame appeared, spread rapidly; and the bomber, ablaze from end to end, crashed into the sea.

The men cheered wildly. Captain Slocombe scarcely had time to feel relief before vaguely hearing the voice of his Third Officer, which seemed to his deadened eardrums to come from a great distance.

"Look, sir—torpedo! Just missed us!"

The Captain followed the pointing finger. Sure enough, there in the water was the foaming wake of a torpedo, seeming to come from right under the bow of the *Montcalm*. It had missed them by only a few feet. But, sparing the Canadian vessel, it flashed like a silver knife towards a ship close on the icebreaker's port side.

The men in the *Montcalm* yelled frantic but utterly useless warning. The torpedo struck home. Flames leaped high out of the after hatch of the doomed ship; and burning debris showered the decks of the *Montcalm*.

His heart numbed by the sight of the mounting flames, in which many of his fellow-seamen were dying, the Captain forced himself to look towards the Commodore's ship, off to starboard. To his dismay he saw that it too had been hit and was already listing. Still farther off, the Vice-Commodore's ship also was fated to a grave in Arctic waters.

"Look at that ship go, sir," said a voice behind him.

Captain Slocombe turned. There the ship which had been torpedoed was standing on end, all ablaze. As they watched, she disappeared beneath the waves, not more than ten of fifteen seconds after the torpedo had struck. The swift and complete destruction of a fellow ship was like a personal loss to every man on board. The Captain thought again of his home and loved ones, so far away. Their world was not this world, where, locked in the

There the ship which had been torpedoed
was standing on end, all ablaze.

bitter cold, man had to endure the full fury of the elements combined with the most devastating of man-made horrors. He saw in the faces of the men about him—men who had faced this sort of thing many times while he was facing it for the first time—renewed and dreadful wonder at a power of destruction so terrible that it could sink three ships in the heart of a convoy at the rate of a ship per minute. What, thought the Captain, was to prevent the enemy from attacking again and again until every ship in the convoy had been destroyed? Yes, indeed, Toronto and comfort and sanity seemed very far away. Still, as he glanced again at the steadfast bearing of every man of his crew, he felt privileged to share danger and dare death with men such as these who, by choice, accepted danger and death as their daily duty.

There was but little time for longing or reflection. With the Commodore's and Vice-Commodore's ships gone, the convoy lacked leaders and was momentarily in confusion. But soon the Rear Commodore's ship took charge, flying the signal,

"Re-form convoy as soon as possible".

There were a few moments of manoeuvring, moments that taxed all the skill and seamanship of a skipper, as other ships moved into the gaps left by the sunken vessels. Then the convoy, once more in order, proceeded on its way.

One by one the cold dim hours slid by, but no more planes came over. In the grey chill of a northern dawn, the skipper, overcome by what had seemed ages of constant strain, slumped on a settee in the chart-room and slept.

Morning passed uneventfully. Later in the afternoon the Captain, refreshed by his briefly snatched rest, was back on the watch once more. Presently, with that now familiar quickening of his pulse, he saw the flutter of the grim black signal flag—enemy planes again!

But although this was an attack by dive bombers, the *Montcalm* escaped scot-free; for it was only the far end of the convoy which actually came under fire.

At last the rugged, snow-capped hills that steeply line Kola Inlet, emerged from the northern mists. And so the C. G. S. *Montcalm* slid safely into the harbour of Murmansk. The long struggle was over, and the transfer of the icebreaker accomplished, in the teeth of storm and gale, ice and cold; against danger of collision or explosion; against peril from the air, from the sea, and from beneath the waves.

The Captain's duty eventually recalled him to his desk in Toronto. But never far from his mind were memories of the voyage that was now a thing of the past. He remembered the stout-hearted seamen once under his command. No doubt they were facing the same desperate risks and enduring the same bitter hardships on yet another voyage.

Later, when His Majesty was pleased to create Captain Slocombe a Member of the British Empire (M.B.E.), he, accepting the honour for his crew as for himself, repeated often in spoken and written words the story of their exploit. With every repetition, the skipper emphasized his aim—to illustrate to the Canadian people, by stirring example, how men of the Merchant Navy faithfully attended to any "great matter" on the high seas.

One time or a hundred times, one voyage or a hundred voyages, the hazards, the hardships were always present. Captain Slocombe, like his brother skippers and their valiant crews, knew that, whatever the task assigned them, he and they would echo always in their hearts the prayer of that old sea-dog: ". . . Grant us also to know that it is not the beginning but the continuing of the same, until it is thoroughly finished, which yieldeth the true glory . . ."

ILS NE PASSERONT PAS

XI

THE DECEMBER night was dark and cold. Chill winds blew over the hills and down into the gullies of central Italy. Sometimes they carried with them great gusts of sleet and icy rain. All the ground in this part of the country was deep in frozen mud.

Camped on a spot of this muddy earth, with constant gun-fire thundering in their ears, a group of Canadian soldiers earnestly talked over plans for the coming dawn.

One of these men was a young French Canadian Captain, a Company Commander in the famous Le Royal 22e Regiment (formerly the Royal 22nd Regiment), the unit of Canada's late General Georges Vanier, Governor-General of Canada. He was Captain (acting Major) Paul Triquet, who had spent his early years at Cabano, Quebec, and enlisted at Montreal. His was the task of leading a Company of fellow-countrymen in a dawn attack. The enemy held strong positions in the hills, and in the stone farmhouses characteristic of that part of Italy.

At midnight of this dreary 14th of December, 1943, Captain Triquet was talking with Major Smith. This officer was Commander of the tank squadron that was to support the attack.

"See here," said Captain Paul, tracing out dark lines on an army map spread before them. "Here is the Moro River we have just crossed. Over here is the port of

Ortona on the Adriatic Sea. The Germans hold it in strength and can't afford to lose it. But it is very important to us also. Therefore we must take it. But, here, between, in this gully and among these ridges, are many enemy troops, tanks and machine-guns."

"And here," said Major Smith, pointing to a couple of dots on the map, "these are stone farm-houses—the village of Casa Berardi at the cross-roads. That is our job for tomorrow—to get control of the cross-roads. Right?"

So, throughout the long dark hours, plans and preparations were made for the dangerous work on the morrow.

Next morning, at the grey hour of seven-thirty, this Company of the Royal 22e set out across the rough and muddy country. Captain Triquet spoke quietly to his men as they pressed forward through the tangled grape-vines, fallen vine-posts, and olive groves.

They had not gone far when suddenly the sharp rat-tat-tat of enemy guns shattered the morning quiet. Shells screeched high in the air above them and ploughed deep into the earth. The fight was going to be bitter.

Captain Triquet shouted his orders. The men took cover wherever they could. At once, from gullies, hillsides, ridges, and even from smoking shell-craters, Canadian guns blazed in telling answer.

Presently the unremitting and well-directed fire took effect. One by one the enemy guns were silenced. The Canadians rushed forward. The first German outpost was captured and fifteen German soldiers surrendered.

Captain Triquet's Company had suffered severely, however. Many of his men had fallen, wounded or killed. Seeing that the Germans would fiercely resist the Canadian advance, the Captain signalled for Major Smith's tanks to follow in. Soon the unwieldy monsters were rumbling over the muddy slopes, protecting the men of the infantry.

The wounded were carried to the shelter of ruined and empty farm-houses. Captain Paul seemed to be everywhere. Here he spoke a cheery word of comfort to a casualty. There he gave a quick order to fill in the gap left by a fallen soldier; and the remainder of the gallant Company pushed forward.

Suddenly, the roar of enemy tanks was heard above the din of battle. Just a few hundred yards away, two of them were lumbering up from a gully. Nearby, still another one manoeuvred into place behind a farm-house. They opened fire.

"Never mind them! They can't shoot, anyway," the Captain shouted, leading his men down into the shelter of another ravine in the valley. The enemy guns blazed away, but most of their fire passed over the heads of the Canadians.

Again Major Smith moved in closer with his eight tanks. The Captain rallied his men into sheltered places around the huge machines, and soon two of the German tanks were put out of action.

Captain Triquet moved among his men from group to group. Seemingly heedless of his own danger, he spoke cheerfully to one here and another there.

"Are you all right there, Henri?" he called to a young private alone beside his Bren gun.

"Yes, sir," was the quick answer. "Don't worry, sir, they won't get through here."

"That's the stuff, Henri. Carry on." And the gallant officer strode firmly on to another group. The air was thick with bullets. Shells burst, showering him with earth and debris, yet he went about his task spreading his own cheerful courage as he went.

Soon the Germans withdrew into the shelter of a small wood. Captain Triquet sent back a wireless message requesting artillery support. He asked that the big guns rake the sheltering trees with their fire. With the attention of the enemy taken up by this artillery attack, the Captain hoped to push forward towards the cross-roads.

Shrewdly, he reasoned that a smoke screen would allow safer and swifter movement. So, once again, he signalled to Major Smith for the tanks. Soon they were thundering along the highway, puffs of smoke billowing behind them. Behind this friendly cloud, the men moved rapidly up the hard road. Like grumbling iron monsters, the tanks rumbled along with them and on to Casa Berardi.

Shortly after noon, the Canadians neared the crossroads. Captain Triquet looked over his Company. Of the 80 soldiers who had started out that morning, only 21 were left. All his officers had been killed or wounded. The supply of ammunition was very low. His wireless set was out of action. The Captain, getting in touch with Major Smith, sent a wireless report on the plight of his Company to Headquarters, by the tank set. Back came the answering message;

"Hold your position at all costs and wait for reinforcements."

It was now two-thirty in the afternoon. The German fire became heavier again. The attacks seemed to come from all sides now. A little ground had been gained, however, and Captain Triquet felt that it was necessary to make a stand again. The six remaining tanks were formed into a circle. The Captain gathered his men and ordered them to dig in around the tanks. From this position, they fought off savage assaults all that long afternoon.

Just at six o'clock a Company of reinforcements reached the weary men. Cheered by this arrival, they rallied round their tireless officer and tried to move farther along the road. However, this was not possible in the gathering darkness and under such deadly enemy fire.

"Well, we'll just stop here until daylight, men." The Captain passed the order from group to group, speaking a word of praise, talking and even laughing in the very face of death.

So the long December night passed for this small group of Canadians huddled on a sleet-coated road in far-off Italy. Back home in Canada the lighted streets and houses, the glistening snowbanks and tinkling sleigh bells, held promise of Christmas cheer, but here in the mud and cold and dark lurked the enemy. The slightest movement intensified the barrage. All night the sombre blue of the sky was streaked with shell bursts and travelling flares of light. The unsleeping Germans were vigilant, waiting for daylight.

In the icy chill and desolation of four o'clock on a winter's morning, two other reinforcement Companies came up. The Captain once more organized his small band and planned their next attack. This was for first light, at seven o'clock.

When the hour arrived, they set out again towards the cross-roads. The Germans opened up at once, their fire knifing through the fading shadows. The Canadians replied. Shells whistled and bullets whined and twanged back and forth over the shivering, twisted olive trees. Throughout another day the battle raged. Then another night of cold, hunger and exhaustion closed over the gallant little group.

During the night hours, the Germans brought up reinforcements. The sounds of their arrival reached the Canadians and warned them of fierce battling on the morrow. Simultaneously the thunder of more advancing tanks echoed across the hills. Captain Triquet stiffened sharply and listened a moment.

"Relax, boys," he laughed. "They're ours—and we can sure use them."

And so it was. A tank reinforcement group had got through and was coming to their aid.

Besides new fighting strength, this group brought ammunition, and—better still—food. The hungry men ate their first real meal in two days. Like any of us, after rest and food, they were strengthened and encouraged to greater effort.

Captain Triquet knew that the enemy were bitterly determined to wipe out his gallant band, rather than give up the cross-roads.

"They *must* give up," the young Canadian vowed grimly.

"Men!" he shouted, striding through the ranks. "The

. . . he dashed forward, pausing only to grasp a new weapon and a fresh supply of ammunition.

enemy are in front of us, behind us, and on our flanks. There is only one safe place. The cross-roads!"

So saying, he dashed forward, pausing only to grasp a new weapon and a fresh supply of ammunition. Often forced to struggle hand to hand with the enemy, he plunged on. Inspired, his men followed. So, inch by inch, in spite of repeated enemy counter-attacks, the now famous Berardi cross-roads were reached.

The last German gun was silenced in the gaunt, ruined farm-house overlooking the cross-roads. Canadian guns poked their black muzzles from the smoke-blackened window frames.

The Germans, gathering all their scattered strength, launched violent attacks at the farm-house. But large reinforcements for the Canadians were even then on the way, their passage cleared by Captain Triquet's Company and the tanks. As the men of the Royal 22e Regiment fiercely repelled the German onslaughts, Captain Triquet called out again and again to his men. He spoke in his and their French mother-tongue the words that had inspired them so often during these past days of terror. These words had become a battle-cry. Like the thrilling call of a bugle, they had stirred the men to fresh courage and effort. Now, at the moment of victory, of holding hard-won gains, they rang once more from the Captain's parched lips.

"Ils ne passeront pas!" (They shall not pass.)

And they did not pass. The Canadian Army in Italy, and their Allied brothers-in-arms, pushed on to Ortona and fresh triumphs.

The road to those victories was made easier, and success more certain, by the bravery of Captain Paul Triquet.

Later, when spring came to Italy and the warm sun shone over the vine-covered ridges, Paul Triquet, now Major Paul Triquet, was in England. One day he received a very important message. It told him to go at once to Buckingham Palace.

Major Triquet knew well what that message meant.

He knew that he was to be honoured with his country's highest award for service on the battle-field. He was justly proud.

Soon he stood in battle-dress before His Majesty the King. As the bronze Victoria Cross was pinned to his tunic, we know Paul Triquet honoured in his heart the men who had rallied to his cry—*"Ils ne passeront pas!"*

PADRE X

XII

WELL, SIR, I hear there's a big move coming up."

The Reverend John Foote, Honorary Captain in the Canadian Army overseas, was talking with his Commanding Officer on a warm summer evening. The Presbyterian clergyman, born in Madoc, Ontario, was Minister or Chaplain of the Royal Hamilton Light Infantry.

"Oh, just a little exercise, padre—routine, you know," replied Lieutenant-Colonel R. H. Labatt, Commanding Officer of the Regiment.

The Chaplain smiled a little.

"Mind if I go along?" he asked. "I really need some exercise."

The Colonel hesitated. He knew very well that the coming "exercise" was no mere routine. So, indeed, did Captain Foote. For this was the summer of 1942, and the great and secretly planned raid on enemy-held Dieppe was soon to take place.

"Oh, I don't think you would be interested." The Colonel spoke lightly, trying to discourage his friend. He knew that the task ahead would be dangerous, and especially so for an Honorary Officer, who does not carry arms in battle.

But the padre was persistent.

"Well, just as you say, of course. But I believe I know something of what lies ahead. I believe, too, that I can help. I'm determined to go along somehow, even if you arrest me for disobedience. So you might as well give your permission and make use of me."

Perhaps he said it jokingly, knowing how serious is the offence of disobedience in the Army, but he won his point. The Colonel consented and the Chaplain went to France.

On the night of the eighteenth of August, 1942, Captain Foote was with his men in one of the more than 200 craft that slipped quietly across the English Channel. The task given to the men of his Regiment was to land on the main beach of the one-time summer resort. If possible, it was to be a surprise attack on the French coastal town then in enemy hands. Through the clear August night, the great fleet ploughed its way. All was as quiet as a peace-time cruise of sleeping travellers. But not many of the passengers in these darkened vessels were sleeping. Everyone glowed with eager excitement, awaiting the coming day and the first Canadian chance to strike a telling blow at the enemy. Here and there throughout the ship, the tall, broad-shouldered figure of the padre was to be seen. With a cheery bit of encouragement for one group, and a little joking with another, he made the men feel that, whatever the dawn might bring, he was their comrade, ready and able to help them.

The purple night clouds began to lighten into grey. The long dark shadows of the ships showed more plainly on the smooth water. Away to the east, faintly glowing streaks showed in the sky. Just ahead loomed the rocky coastline of France.

"There it is, boys."

The men whispered hoarsely in the tense excitement. The great fleet spread out and straightened into a grim line. This threatening dark shadow swept silently in towards shore, heavy engines throttled down to a low throbbing. Still no sign of action from the town twinkling peacefully with small dots of light. Yet every man knew that, among the jagged rocks rising at either side of the town, ugly German guns looked out over the Channel.

"Even now," thought Captain Foote, "perhaps those black muzzles are aimed at us."

He looked about him at the young eager faces, pale in the breaking dawn. As he looked, he felt very proud, for not a face showed lack of courage. Nevertheless, he felt sad, too, as he wondered what daylight would bring to them. How well and bitterly the padre was to know before the shadows of another night drew in again!

"Board the landing-boats," the order came.

The men were well trained and quickly they scrambled into places in the square-nosed craft. The small open boats drifted quietly in to shore, scarcely making a splash as they nudged up into the sand. Before the boats had grounded, the men sprang out and scrambled up the beach.

A fury of noise burst from the skies and all about them. Allied planes roared overhead, coming in according to plan to cover the attack. The guns of the Navy thundered from the sea, and friendly, protecting smoke-screens, laid down by the naval and air support, drifted over the Canadians. By this time, of course, the enemy were fully aroused. The wide black mouths of the big guns spat their hatred over the beach. Smaller guns, from the town itself, raked the gravelled stretch with fire. The men fought fiercely through this terrible ordeal, but many staggered and dropped in the blast.

Meantime the padre, carrying no weapon whatsoever, made his way to the regimental first-aid post, which had been set up in a little sheltered hollow. Here the fire from the guns was just as fierce, but the dip in the beach gave a little cover to men lying prone. The padre remained on his feet, however, along with the brave medical officers, who worked, careless of the firing, to ease the pain of the wounded and dying.

"Look out there," shouted the padre, "that poor chap stumbling towards us can't make it."

There on the open beach, a wounded man was struggling to the shelter. He staggered, fell, rose to his knees, crawled and dropped again. The stretcher-bearers were all busy farther up the beach. Inside the aid post, the doctors and their helpers had more than they could do. No one seemed able to go to the help of the poor fellow dragging himself along so close to shelter. It was no time for words. Captain Foote, snatching up a first-aid kit, dashed from the slight shelter into open view. Bullets skittered in the gravel all around him. Shells whined low over his head. Still he ran on.

"Hold on, lad, I'm getting there," he called to the stricken man.

At last he reached him. But the soldier was past hearing his words of comfort. Badly wounded and in great pain, he lay still, unable to help himself at all. The Chaplain was no doctor. He scarcely knew what to do. He glanced down the shell-swept beach. Not far away, a stretcher party was moving. He signalled wildly and saw that he had been noticed. Paying no attention to the battle raging about him, Captain Foote gave what simple aid he could to the wounded soldier.

The man, his pain eased a little, heard and felt something of the comfort the padre was trying to give.

"Thanks, padre," he gasped.

The stretcher party got to them at last. Gently they lifted the soldier and started back to the first-aid post. All the way, the Chaplain moved beside the suffering man, giving him strength and courage.

Hour after hour the battle raged on. Hour after hour, the padre carried on with his heroic work, never faltering. At last the long morning drew to an end. The tide went out from the beach and the officers in the aid post decided to move. Not far from their poor shelter, one of the landing-craft was grounded. It certainly offered more cover than did the hollow on the open beach.

So began the difficult task of carrying the wounded men to the new refuge. Captain Foote was one of the

Paying no attention to the battle which raged about him, Captain Foote gave what simple aid he could . . .

first to move out with the stretcher-bearers. Time after time, he made the short but perilous trip. Above the frenzy of noise, he shouted words of encouragement whenever a lull allowed.

"We'll soon be there, my boy," or, "Cheer up, it can't go on for ever,"—or perhaps just a word of sympathy to comfort the wounded.

At last the commanders saw that nothing more could be gained. The order to return to the landing-craft was flashed from ship to shore. Wireless sets picked up the message and passed it on. Slowly, painfully, the exhausted little band fought their way back step by step across the gravelled beach. The terrible German guns still barked and blasted, although many had been destroyed by the Canadians. Many soldiers fell wounded within sight of the boats that were to take them to safety. Captain Foote, completely heedless of his own danger, crossed and re-crossed the death-ridden stretch of beach helping man after man to the shelter of the landing-craft.

One by one, the boats were filled and drew out to the ships waiting to carry survivors back to England. Time after time, the gallant Chaplain was urged to take a place in one of these boats.

"Come on, padre; there's room here for you," someone would call.

"No thanks, lad, I'm not quite ready to leave yet," the padre would answer.

Finally, all the sea-worthy craft had drawn away from the beach. Many soldiers and their officers stayed behind, still fighting fiercely. They knew very well that only death or capture by the enemy awaited them. Yet they chose to stand firm, protecting, as well as they could, their departing comrades.

As one of the last of the small boats pushed off from the gravel, a place was made for Captain Foote in it.

"Here you are, padre—right in here," called a soldier, clearing a small place near him.

"All right, chum. I'll be right with you. Just wait till I

help this poor chap in," answered the Captain.

But when the "poor chap" was safely in, the Captain turned away and ran back up the beach, while the space between boat and shore widened swiftly.

"I'm staying with the men," he shouted after the disappointed crew in the boat. "They might need me a while yet."

As long as the ammunition lasted, the Canadians gave the Germans blast for blast. As long as the firing lasted, men fell wounded. As long as men fell wounded, Captain Foote and his fellow-officers carried on their work of giving aid and comfort. But it could not go on for ever. As hot noon passed into afternoon, the Canadian fire gradually slackened off.

The home-going ships grew smaller and smaller in the distance. The noise of the "air umbrella" of planes covering the fleet died away over the Channel. By ones and twos, the weary fighters were taken prisoner by the Germans. Night closed in over the smoking devastation of Dieppe.

Next day, the same sun that had shone above the fury of the raid on the gravelled beach, rose over an exhausted, battle-shocked little band. Trudging along a French road, inland from the coastal town, the men were herded along towards far-off prison camps. Among them tramped a tall, cheerful man *with bare feet!* It was the Regimental Chaplain.

The day before, as he plunged time and again through the surf, carrying men to the landing-craft, his heavy boots had become water-soaked. Thinking to make better time without their sodden weight, the Captain had pulled them off. He had not afterwards had a chance to put them on again. So for two days, he marched bare-footed. Over broken stone, cinders of railway tracks, and rough ground, the German captors led the prisoners. Yet the padre continued to be an example of endurance and courage to his comrades. Finally, Colonel Labatt, his Commanding Officer, who was also a prisoner, managed to get hold of a pair of French army boots. Gratefully, the weary Chaplain drew them on, over his bruised and bleeding feet. They were large and unwieldy, yet Captain Foote treasured them as a prized possession.

At last, after many dreary days, Captain Foote with other officers of his regiment arrived at a prison camp called Oflag VIIB. This was one of the German prisons for officers only. In such a camp the prisoners were a little better off for special privileges were allowed to officers. But even here the padre did not rest. Instead, at the very first opportunity, he requested and was granted a transfer to one of the "Stalag" camps for "other ranks". Simply, he explained his action by saying that the men needed him. So, for two long years, Captain Foote carried on his unselfish service to the men with him.

Meantime, the story of Dieppe was blazoned round the world. Huge black headlines streamed across newspaper front pages. Canadian heroism in battle was told and retold. Among the many glorious reports, there appeared often the story of the unknown Chaplain who had appeared in the thick of battle—a sturdy angel of mercy. Who was "Padre X"?

So a legend grew about the Canadian Chaplain. Nearly a year later, there were some rumours of the identity of Padre X. It was not, however, until 12 February, 1946, that real recognition came. On that date, Captain Foote (later Major) became the first member of the Canadian Chaplain Services to wear the Victoria Cross.

Canadians cheered and were proud of Honorary Major John Weir Foote, V.C. Officers and men who carry memories of the Dieppe beach and German Stalags perhaps say less. Yet each man will remember for ever the kindly hands and cheery voice of Padre X.

WHO RIDE THE SKIES

XIII

"Almighty God, Who makest the clouds Thy chariot and Who walkest upon the wings of the wind, we commend to Thy Fatherly protection all who ride the skies in the service of the Fleet and those in whose work they trust."

—Prayer used in the Fleet Air Arm.

THE SKY is a lonely place. So also is the mighty ocean. Those who follow their duty in either sky or sea must be, indeed, of a high courage and faith. Many brave lads risked their lives on the land, in the air, and on the waters of the deep, during the great world conflict of 1939-1945. They went forth in groups, in companies, and in armies. Shoulder to shoulder, they met and conquered strange perils, giving to each other strength and comradeship as they faced what has always been fearsome to mankind—the Unknown.

But "Hammy" Gray was one of those who went alone. Upon graduation from University of British Columbia in 1940, he joined the Canadian Naval Services. As an Ordinary Seaman, he learned the stern and ancient rules of those who play the game with Father Neptune. He was one of a class of 75 Canadians chosen from all parts of Canada for training with the Royal Navy. Again, later, he was one of 19 Canadians selected to serve with the Fleet

Air Arm, whose men must be airmen as well as sailors. So Hammy Gray became a pilot in the Fleet Air Arm. He guided his aircraft off the deck of a Fleet carrier in mid-ocean, to search the seas for enemy shipping. His duty took him through British waters, into enemy-infested Mediterranean seas, and off the coast of South Africa. He acquired great skill in mastering this special service, and in 1942 he became Lieutenant Robert Hampton Gray of the R.C.N.V.R. (Royal Canadian Naval Volunteer Reserve).

Early in 1944, Hammy came home on overseas leave. His friends and comrades welcomed him warmly and, of course, asked about his life in the Service.

"Oh, just great," Hammy would reply, "but I'm still waiting for the big day."

"Big day?" they asked. "Seems as though you've had a lot of big days already, by all accounts."

Hammy smiled faintly. "Ah, no—not really—just routine," he said quietly. "What I'm waiting for is a chance at those Japs. We thought we would catch them off the African coast, but nary a sight did we get. But we'll follow them right to Tokyo Bay if we have to."

And that is what he did.

Upon returning to England after his leave, Lieutenant Gray was appointed to service with H.M.S. *Formidable,* a very important aircraft carrier. He joined the ship as a fighter pilot, and within a few days, he was eagerly taking part in great and dangerous operations.

There was, at that time, a German sea-marauder doing much damage to Allied shipping. This was the battleship *Tirpitz.* The huge, lurking sea-monster pursued convoys and wreaked havoc among them. Then, slipping with cunning and speed away from the scene of disaster, she would hide out in some sheltered enemy-controlled harbour while Allied avengers, on the seas and from the skies, sought her in vain.

When H.M.S. *Formidable* took up the chase in August, 1944, Lieutenant Gray went with his ship. The *Tirpitz* had managed to escape through grey North Sea waters to a hide-out in the rocky Norwegian coast. Driving through heavy seas, H.M.S. *Formidable* followed.

Suddenly, a reconnaissance aircraft gave the warning. The German raider had been spotted riding at anchor in a secure refuge. The natural rockiness of the inlet was in itself a safeguard, and all around, along the coast and up in the hills, were light and heavy enemy guns. On H.M.S. *Formidable,* the aircraft awaited the signal for take-off. The pipe for action stations sounded over the ship's broadcast system. The planes rose in the elevators from their hangars to the flight-deck. With their wings folded back they looked like giant moths resting before winging away into the sky. Seamen pushed them into position and deck crews spread the wings for flight.

Gray was leader of his section. He climbed into the cockpit and started his engine. The Flight Commander signalled from his platform with a pair of coloured flags. Hammy wheeled his plane into place and waited while the ship steamed into proper position for the fighters to take off.

Again the Commander signalled, this time with a green flag. Smoothly, Lieutenant Gray's plane roared along the deck and was airborne. At intervals, the others followed him, and soon they were zooming over the big guns on the coast below.

The growl of engines rose to a shriek. Like angry bees, the planes swarmed down over the gun-posts, with Hammy Gray in the lead. The guns barked and puffs of smoke and orange flame burst all around them. Nevertheless, down they went.

Boom-m—! Black smoke rose from the coast-line. One gun-post was silenced. Gray and his followers dived again. Again the thunder of explosions below echoed in the clouds. Skilfully diving, lifting, swerving, Lieutenant Gray led his section through the dense gun-fire from the coast. At last, the task seemed to be finished. The young Lieutenant signalled return to base and they headed back to the H.M.S. *Formidable.* Behind them in the Norwegian inlet, smoking and disabled guns left the way open for torpedo attacks on the *Tirpitz* lying there.

But the enemy were still strong in the stormy North Atlantic. Three German destroyers were sighted in the bay, and again Gray led in attacking them. Again he dared the bitter anti-aircraft fire as he swooped and circled, blasting and crippling the enemy ships. His plane was hit, finally, and most of the rudder was carried away. It looked as though the gallant Canadian must plunge helplessly into the sea. But while anxious eyes watched from planes and mother ship, he glided his wounded craft back to the deck, judged his approach correctly, and, at last, landed safely.

The skilful and courageous leadership of the young Canadian could not escape the attention of watchful Senior Officers. Indeed, so outstanding did it appear to these men, accustomed as they were to brave deeds, that they mentioned Lieutenant Gray in despatches. This brought to him the bronze oak leaf which is the symbol of such an honour. In the words of the citation of the Mention in Despatches, Gray showed "undaunted courage, skill and determination".

But this was only the beginning. The next year, 1945, brought victory over Germany. Still there was Japan, off in the blue Pacific Ocean. Her warships threatened our Allied sea-lanes.

The navies combined their efforts once more and formed the Allied Pacific Fleet. In April, 1945, H.M.S. *Formidable* steamed away into southern waters to join the British Pacific Fleet near Okinawa. Lieutenant Gray was to have his chance at the Japs after all—his Big Day.

In July, the Canadian pilot led his section in attacks on Japanese airfields near Tokyo. On the 24th day of the month, he led a force to the inland sea around Japan, badly damaging a merchant ship and blasting two seaplane bases and an airfield. Four days later, he led an attack on more shipping, this time destroying and sinking an enemy vessel. Again his senior officers took note of his work. Again a report of his skill and daring went in to Headquarters. This time the young pilot was honoured with the Distinguished Service Cross. Surely, the brave lad had more than done his duty.

But no. Less than two weeks later, just six days before Japan surrendered, Hammy Gray flew again into the skies over those far-off seas. The fighting was desperate in those closing days of war. Every man in every branch of the Services was straining to bring the bitter struggle to an end. Again H.M.S. *Formidable* moved into the heart of the action. And where the battle was fiercest, there always was Lieutenant Gray.

On this warm summer day of 9 August, 1945, Hammy took off as usual from the deck of the *Formidable*. Riding alone through foreign skies, he looked down and saw the tiny shapes of many ships off the mainland of Japan, in the inlet called Onagowa Wan. These must be damaged or destroyed, but one at a time, carefully. He looked them over.

"There's my target," he decided, noting the grim outlines of a Japanese destroyer.

Down, down sped the little plane. Vicious enemy guns came to life on ships and shore. The Lieutenant's plane was hit. It seemed to waver a little, uncertainly. Presently, he steadied it and swept on. Again the plane shuddered, almost out of control. Still the pilot drove fearlessly on to his target, while the enemy fire trapped him in a net of flame.

Closer and closer he came to the long, grey destroyer. His plane caught fire and flames licked along the wings.

There! The blazing aircraft hung over the doomed ship, just about fifty feet away. There was no one to whom the young Canadian could sing out:

"Bombs away!"

No comrade called to him:

"This is it. Cheerio, old boy!"

But the bombs fell whistling through the air. Straight to

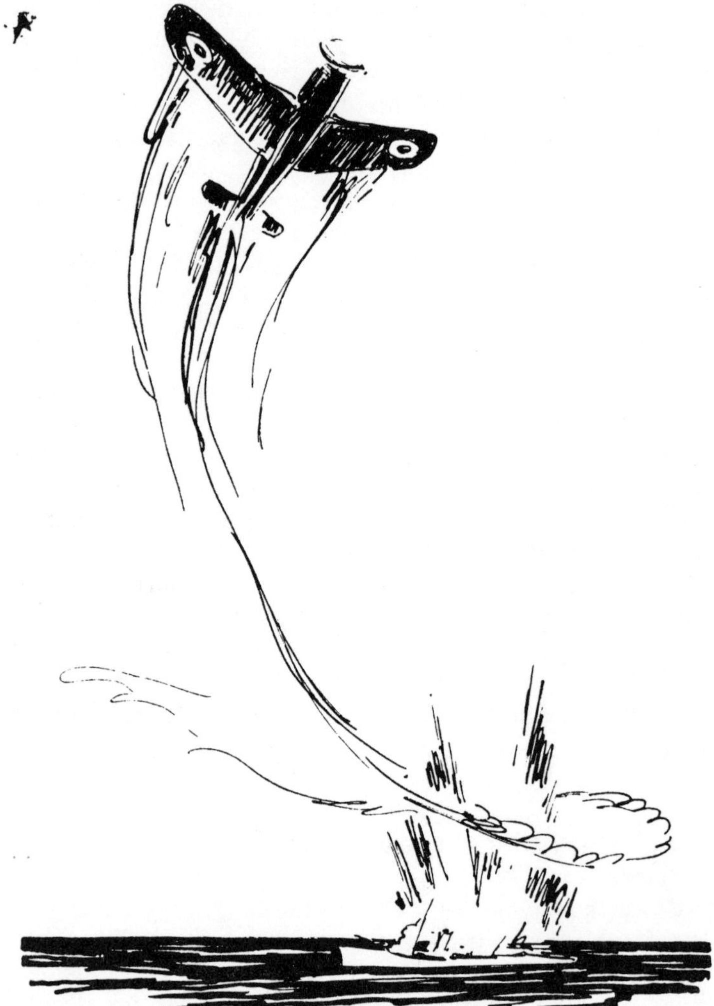

The bombs fell whistling through the air. Straight to their target they went, with faultless aim.

their target they went with faultless aim.

Crash-h-h! Smoke, flame, debris and water were hurled high into the sky, sank down again into the churning waves of the bay. Only a welter of wreckage, oil and smoke remained of the grey sea-wolf.

Above the turmoil, the little plane struggled, blazed, and plunged into the sea.

Lieutenant Robert Hampton Gray had lived his Big Day —and his last.

For the third time, senior officers sent to Headquarters a glowing report of the young Canadian. For the third time His Majesty the King was pleased to honour his "fighting spirit, inspired leadership . . . unforgettable example".

"Hammy" Gray did not live to wear the Victoria Cross, yet in deathless records his name goes down—Lieutenant Robert Hampton Gray, V.C., D.S.C., Royal Canadian Naval Volunteer Reserve. On the Halifax Memorial he is listed among those war dead "having no known grave", but at the Canadian Forces Base at Sheerwater (formerly H.M.C.S.) a permanent marker bears his name—the dependents' school for the married quarters.

As summers return again and again to home and foreign skies, people the world over know that he, and others like him who rode the skies in lonely peril, did not ride in vain.

A CHRISTMAS PRESENT FOR "MOM"

XIV

IT WAS a warm night in early October. A sturdy dark-haired lad strode down a broad street in New Westminster, British Columbia. He whistled a gay Irish tune, keeping step with the jig as he went along.

"Hey, Ernie!" A friendly voice hailed him from across the street. "You all ready for the meet tomorrow?"

"You bet!" the stocky lad replied. He stopped at the edge of the sidewalk, teetering back and forth on the curb.

"What're you going in this time, Ernie—the half-mile again?"

"Sure thing!" Ernie Smith was a fellow who knew his own mind.

"Bet you'll win it. Guess Trapp Tech. is in pretty good form this year. You ever think of going professional in athletics, Ernie?"

"Aw no, I'm not nearly good enough. I just try it for fun."

"Well, anyhow, good luck, Ernie. Hope you make out all right."

"Oh, well, I'll have a good try. I'd sure like to take the Senior Cup home to Mom. She's proud of all that stuff, you know."

Next day was fine, with just a trace of autumn coolness in the air. A great many high-school students, with their teachers and friends, were gathered to watch the New Westminster inter-collegiate track-meet. The half-mile foot race was announced. Ernie Smith was among the boys waiting behind the start line.

"On your mark!"

The boys toed the line.

"Get set!"

They crouched in position.

"Go!"

Away they went, with a flash of brown legs.

Ernie ran easily at first. Two boys, getting into their stride early, were well ahead of him on the first lap.

Ernie was not worried, until he saw that the distance between him and the two ahead was widening. At the same time, he heard, close over his shoulder, the crunch-crunch of the flying feet of the boy behind him. He shortened and quickened his stride, settling down to real effort. The boy behind him gained, drew level, and began to forge ahead.

For a second or two, Ernie began to lose heart. Then he remembered his words of the night before. "Mom's proud of all that stuff." All right, Mom *would* be proud!

His running-shoes drummed the cinders with a quick steady beat. His muscles began to ache and burn. The blood roared and pounded through his head, and his chest ached with every gasping breath. But on he raced. The finish line stretched whitely across in front of him, and at last he was out in front.

Forcing his straining muscles even beyond their strength, Ernie Smith flung himself across the finish line —the winner.

* * * *

Thirteen years have passed quickly over the head of the boy who brought glory to T. J. Trapp Technical School. We find him now in far-off Italy, Private Ernest Alvia Smith of The Seaforth Highlanders of Canada. For, although October has come again, the year is 1944 and

Pte. Smith is fighting, with his comrades, against the German hordes in a strange land.

At some time in the years following that school track-meet in New Westminster, Ernie Smith was nicknamed Smokey. As Smokey Smith, he won another and far greater victory.

The night was dark and wet. The soldiers had been slogging through Italian rain and mud for many days. Men of the Seaforth Highlanders of Canada, and their comrades in another famous Canadian Regiment, the Princess Patricia's Canadian Light Infantry, were in the Italian town of Cesena, just few miles from the shores of the Adriatic Sea.

Canadians had captured Cesena that twentieth day of October. But, although the enemy had been cleared from the centre of the place, there was still a great deal of heavy fighting to be done in the outskirts.

The narrow River Savio ran through the western part of the town. On the other side of this stream, many Germans were entrenched. Allied troops had to cross over and establish a bridgehead on the other bank; that is, to drive out the Germans and entrench themselves strongly in their place. This would mean that bridges could be built over the stream, allowing many more soldiers, tanks, and heavy equipment to cross.

Pte. Smith was a member of a specially trained tank-hunting group. This group, or platoon, was to follow the first attacking parties and give them protection from German tanks and big guns.

On the night of the twentieth, men of the Princess Pats made a brave attempt to cross the stream. German gunfire was very fierce, and many soldiers fell, wounded or killed. Some reached the other side, however, and strove to hold positions there against violent opposition.

The tank-hunters were waiting orders to follow. All day, from the tower of a church on the Canadian-held bank of the river, the men waited and watched. The battle raged on the other bank.

Darkness came early and, soon after, rain began to fall drearily again.

"Rain and mud, mud and rain. Pretty grim, isn't it?" one of the lads grumbled.

"It's dry enough in here where we are," said Smokey, glancing out through the rain towards the farther river bank.

Everyone knew what he meant. They were all waiting to get out there and share the danger and discomfort of battle. Yet hearts often thumped a little harder as the heavy guns roared and the earth trembled.

At last the order came.

"Let's get going, fellows," was the only spoken response. The men moved rapidly in pairs and threes to the swollen river. They slithered down the muddy banks through the steady pour of the rain. The water was waist deep, and in mid-stream the current ran swiftly.

After the struggle through the treacherous waters of the stream, worse was to follow. The farther bank was ten to fifteen feet higher than the one they had just left. The driving rain had turned it into a slippery mass that dragged at their heavy boots. Sliding through the ooze, the men gradually gained a foothold at the top and set up their special infantry anti-tank guns.

With an ear-splitting racket, Pte. Smith's company began firing rapidly on the enemy. Suddenly through the constant thunder and whine of artillery fire, there came another sound. Three German Panther tanks were lumbering down the road. A German Staff car, carrying a group of officers, sped ahead.

Smith and his companions were directly in the path of these fearful oncoming monsters. At once Ernie took command of his gun and gunners.

"Here, you two!—across into the field. Come on!"

The men followed him, carrying the heavy PIAT (a short name for the Projector Infantry Anti-Tank Gun).

Within good aiming distance of the German Panthers, they set up their weapon.

When the tanks were almost on top of them, they suddenly opened fire.

"Come on back with me, Jimmy," Smith called to one of the gunners. Followed by his companion, he crossed the road again and took over another PIAT, whose gunner had been wounded.

The enemy tanks came on with frightful determination and speed.

Behind the tanks were heavy guns on tracks (called self-propelled guns) and about thirty soldiers. It was a terrible assault to face, but Smith and his men waited and did not move. When the tanks were almost on top of them, they suddenly opened fire. The anti-tank guns barked once, twice, and again and again. The first tank stopped, damaged but not destroyed. It turned round and retreated down the road. The Staff car was demolished, the German officers killed or wounded. The second tank was hit and blew up with a mighty burst of noise and flame.

The Germans were tossing hand-grenades with all-too-deadly aim. Jimmy, at Smokey's side, was struck down. Ten German soldiers jumped from the Panther, where they had been riding, and rushed on Smith and his comrades. Smokey, without pause, leaped from his place and ran to meet them, firing now with his tommy-gun. The enemy guns blazed, and grenades exploded all around him. Nothing could stop him, it seemed. Four of the Germans fell and the rest turned away from the ferocity of Pte. Smith's attack.

The relief was short-lived. Another tank opened fire. More German infantry closed in on Smith. But he never flinched. Steadfastly firing, while ammunition lasted, he held his ground, a one-man army.

This superb gallantry won the day. The attacking German infantry, completely routed by such super-human courage, turned in disorder and fled.

By this time, one tank and both the heavy guns had been destroyed. Another tank had withdrawn. From some distance back, however, the guns of a third swept the area. Through this fury of noise and spurting flame,

Pte. Smith now sought out his wounded comrade. He half-carried him to the shelter of a nearby building, and bound up his wounds as well as he could.

"You're okay now, Jimmy. Just rest here. I'll be back." With these words, Ernie returned to the battle. But the battle appeared to be over—and won. Although Pte. Smith stood on watchful guard for another enemy attack, no more tanks roared down the road, no German infantry rushed on him with hand-grenades.

Smokey Smith had fought them ten to one, and Smokey Smith was the victor. The objective of the Seaforth Highlanders was gained and held, and an important step forward was taken in the war in Italy.

Just before Christmas, in Buckingham Palace, Pte. Ernest Smith received the Empire's highest award for bravery, the Victoria Cross, from His Majesty The King.

> "By the dogged determination, outstanding devotion to duty and superb gallantry of this private soldier, his comrades were so inspired that the bridgehead was held . . ."

That was what the great feat meant to the Empire, and to the world.

To Ernie Smith it meant something else. When questioned, he said little, just a few words about its being "A nice Christmas present to take home for Mom".

WITHOUT WITNESSES

XV

> "Perfect courage is to do without witnesses what one would be capable of doing with the world looking on."
>
> Duc de la Rochefoucauld.

It was a bright Sunday afternoon early in October, 1944. The sun shone upon a little Canadian Army jeep, chugging along one of the main roads in Belgium. In it were two Canadian army officers from Ottawa, Ontario. One of these, driver of the vehicle, was Captain George Pepper, Official War Artist with the 2nd Canadian Division, Overseas, and his companion, another non-combatant, Historical Officer, Captain Joseph Engler.

On this autumn day, the men were looking for material to be used in the making of Canadian history . . . the written and pictorial story of Canadians in front-line battle. It was about the time of the famous Battle of the Scheldt to free the Belgian port of Antwerp from the German hold. The officers had passed through the town of Brecht where sporadic fighting was continuing, although it was really in Canadian hands.

Leaving Brecht to find a quieter spot farther from the whine of shell fire and the thud of heavy guns, the Canadians drove through the little town of St. Leonard where two main roads stretched about a half mile apart, one running very close to enemy lines. The intention was to drive along the one farther to the south, which ran safely through Canadian-held territory. By some strange twist of fate, however, Captain Engler became confused in the map-reading, and, without knowing it, the two in the jeep bowled smartly along the north road nearest to the German lines.

Both men wore regulation battle dress and helmets. Captain Pepper's helmet was screened with camouflage netting and wound with leaves and grass. Captain Engler carried a rifle and Captain Pepper a small pistol.

Once in a while they passed small groups of soldiers chatting with the country folk. War and the terrors of battle seemed very far away. Cattle grazed in the fields, looking up as the jeep rattled past. Now and then, chickens scattered before them. This was Belgian farm-land. There was nothing in the quiet far-off blue of the sky, or in the twitter of occasional bird-calls to warn them of what was to come.

Soon they reached a cross-roads.

"What's this ahead?" Captain Pepper slowed the jeep a bit.

"Looks like a British patrol. Yes, so it is."

The British party drew to a stop. A few questions were asked and answered.

"Better not go too far this way, sir. You're getting out of our lines," the Britisher said.

"We won't—but all this territory has been cleared by the Canadians," was the confident reply, as the jeep roared into gear and plunged forward.

As yard after yard of countryside rolled by, Captain Pepper's keen blue eyes sought eagerly for picture-subjects. So intent was he on this main purpose that he did not see the lone figure a few yards from the road until he drew even with him. Startled, he drove a few yards further into the shelter of some bushes, stopping the car.

"Say, did you see what I saw?" he asked.

"No, what?"

"A German soldier—back there standing in a slit trench!"

Engler looked startled.

"No! Couldn't be! But—well let's have a look."

"Let's go back and take him prisoner," said Captain Pepper, looking forward to a little excitement. Certainly he did not look in vain.

Next moment they were out of the jeep and creeping carefully back, with pistol and rifle at the ready. As they came out from the shadow of a clump of trees, there he was. Still standing with his back to the road, looking out across the fields to the west, he seemed not to know of their approach. They covered him with their weapons.

"Hands up!" Captain Pepper spoke suddenly.

The German turned swiftly. His arms reached skyward. His mouth fell open and he stood, the picture of astonishment. Canadian soldiers!

"Keep him covered, Joe. I'll relieve him of his weapons." Captain Pepper walked toward the youthful enemy. He motioned him to come forward.

The German climbed out of the slit trench, which was about two feet deep. There were many of these cleverly constructed trenches flanking the roadside and ditches. Some were about two by four feet and four feet deep, just large enough for one man. There was no heap of thrown-up ground to betray the shelter. The one in which the German had been standing was about two feet deep and had sods built up around it.

Captain Pepper's quick glance noticed these details as the German came slowly forward. It was but the work of a moment to loosen the Nazi soldier's bayonet belt, and complete the search.

"Perhaps there are others around. Better have a look," the Canadians decided.

Pepper walked over to the ditch. Just as he bent to look down, a horrible squealing sound stunned his ears. He whirled about to face a startling scene. The other

Canadian officer was on his back, struggling fiercely, with the German on top, giving forth these blood-curdling whinnying cries. Pepper rushed back across the road. It all happened so quickly. While it was impossible to guess by what treacherous twist the German had downed Engler, it was instantly clear from his warning squeals that other Germans were near. The youthful guard certainly would not have defied two armed Canadians and made such a racket had he not known he was in his own territory.

All this flashed through Pepper's mind as he leaped towards the struggling figures. With cocked pistol, he circled the rolling men. It was hard to take aim sure enough to dispose of the German and yet save Engler. He fired once, but wildly. Above the crack of the pistol shrilled the German's continued caterwauling. Engler fought silently, his face twisted with effort. Desperately, with great care, Pepper fired again. The shot told. The screaming stopped and the German rolled over heavily against the front of the jeep. Engler scrambled to his feet.

In that same instant, both men saw the black muzzle of a German rifle poking through the shrubbery across the road. Further along was another—and yet another. A second's glance revealed the grim danger. Both men leaped for the ditch. Already it was too late. The bark of rifle shots cracked in the air.

Engler reached the first trench beside the road and dived into it. Pepper dashed on past him to the one lately sheltering the German guard. This was dug into the bottom of the deep ditch. Rifle shots were still pelting the road and grassy borders.

Spang went the answering fire from Captain Engler's rifle. Pepper could see him leaning forward, lying along the slope of his trench, firing into the hedge across the way. Right at the war artist's own hand lay the German guard's rifle. Aiming at the mouth of the first rifle in the hedge, Pepper fired rapidly, keeping well down in the trench.

Peering carefully over the edge to take aim, Pepper saw Engler lean out of his trench to do likewise. A German rifle cracked. Engler groaned once and slumped back into the trench.

"Joe, Joe—Are you hurt?" cried Pepper. Only silence answered him. Strangely, the German firing ceased. Through the sudden stillness, Pepper heard his comrade breathe hoarsely, rapidly, just a few times, then utter quiet. The artist knew that any shot which reached its mark at all must almost certainly be fatal, with only Engler's head and chest being exposed above the trench.

Seconds, like hours, passed. There he was, alone in the enemy lines, his comrade killed, and just across the road unseen enemy eyes watched behind their guns for his first move. It could only be a matter of minutes, he thought. They would swarm across the road, and haul him from his poor shelter. In the awful loneliness of those seconds, Pepper felt that swift death was his best hope. The body of the German he had killed would surely mark him for Nazi vengeance.

His first thought was of the papers he carried. Letters of instruction and authority signed by high-ranking officials, together with his ordinary identification papers, would provide excellent passport material for enemy spies. Rapidly he pulled the packet from his pocket and thrust it under the sods covering the sides of the trench. His uppermost thought was sadness, the pity and uselessness of it all. It had been such a promising day. Things were going well, and comradeship was good. Now, just a few feet away, his friend lay dead, while he waited alone for that same fate.

But nothing happened! Pepper, his first near-panic past, decided to edge his way along the deep ditch in the direction of his own lines. He might get a few yards, possibly only feet, but it was better than sitting still. The bottom of the ditch was dry earth and fairly clean. For a space he crawled rapidly along on hands and knees. Then, flattening out as much as possible, he edged his way through the tangled weeds and masses of brambles overhanging the ditch. A few feet from the trench, he dropped the German rifle, pushing it hastily into the long grass. With each jerky breath, he expected something to happen, but nothing did and he crawled on with pistol in his hand.

Several minutes passed. He was now some yards away from the scene of the fight. He heard voices behind him on the road and he knew from the sounds that the Germans were looking after their stricken comrade lying against the jeep. Now they would come down the road looking for him. Ahead of him was a square culvert opening under the road. He backed into this, feet first, trying to kick away the loose earth. But it was partly blocked with ground and there was not room enough to shelter him. He crawled out and on. Ahead of him the ditch widened and shallowed. Near the road, at this point, was a large building. It would probably be a Belgian farm house, because it was near the ruins of a burned barn. The family might be friendly to a Canadian soldier. On the other hand, they might not be, and in any case, German soldiers could be billetted there. Peeping up over the ditch, Captain Pepper studied the building. Attached to the house was an oblong structure with a row of frosted windows. This strange bit of architecture puzzled the Canadian officer.

Later, he discovered that it was but the stable part of the farm dwelling, even adjoining as it did the house proper, and that here the farm animals were quartered. At this time, however, the strangeness of it alarmed him. So, seeing another culvert beyond, he wormed his way cautiously through and partly under the thick weeds.

As he approached the possible haven, he saw that it was a cement tiling under a cross-road. The dark mouth of the culvert looked promising. After several minutes, he reached it and crawled inside with thankful relief.

Edging along the narrow cement channel, Captain Pepper came upon what seemed to be solid earth on the other side. Wriggling out into the ditch again, he backed in this time, and kicked at the ground at the far end. It did not appear to yield so the officer decided that the ditch had its beginning here, and that beyond was a solid lawn or yard of the Belgium farmhouse. Later, he found that only a small mound of earth, dumped there for some unknown purpose, had barred his way. This dark and damp shelter was to be his hideout for days while Nazi troopers patrolled over his head.

After screening the entrance with a scattering of straw heaped nearby, Pepper crouched back to review his plight in the temporary refuge. Aside from the peril of his position, there were the everyday considerations of food and drink. Sure that nightfall would enable him to reach his own lines under cover of darkness, his immediate concern was for nourishment to give him strength for the hazard. A search of his pockets yielded a crumpled Chiclet box, with just four of the small squares, the only edible in his possession.

The afternoon shadows slanted beyond his narrow hideout. A few clucking chickens came to scratch in the straw near the entrance. The Captain realized the danger of startling them and so attracting the attention of possible hostile eyes. He lay very still, waiting for the night.

Finally all seemed quiet and dark. Crawling with difficulty, due to cramped muscles, and brambles that scratched and tore, he made his way in the direction of the afternoon battle. After 200 slow and painful yards, the moon suddenly sailed out from behind a cloud bank, flooding the countryside with mellow light. Hastily Pepper retreated to his culvert. The sound of movement caught his attention and, peering through the bushes, he saw a guard patrolling across the road. Tempted to check whether the patrol was friend or enemy, the officer decided the risk was too great, and settled back into the cold discomfort of the culvert. Bolstering his spirits with the thought that Canadian tanks or armored cars would, doubtless, soon come rumbling down the enemy-held road, the War artist dozed while only yards away the Belgian earth suffered the heavy tread of Nazi soldiers.

Days fell into a timeless procession of frustrated attempts to reach safety, and the bitter struggle with desperate physical needs and mental anguish.

Sunday marked the passing of a week of endless hours since the two Canadian officers had rolled confidently along Belgian roads in search of history. Still no reasonably safe chance for escape had presented itself. During that time George Pepper had suffered hunger, thirst, doubts and danger lying in his cement-lined bed, as surely a prisoner of war as if behind barbed-wired walls and guarding enemy guns. The carefully rationed Chiclets served for a meagre few hours before the onslaught of gnawing hunger caused acute distress. Yet even worse, as meal-times came and went, and shrinking stomach dulled appetite, the more vital need for water became urgent. Stretching and wriggling the length of the culvert, searching the damp mud for moisture, brought no relief to the man's thirst-swollen tongue and dry throat. Yet, somewhere beneath that moist earth was—water.

Pepper began to dig. Pausing when his failing strength demanded rest, he chewed the dew-moistened grass at the tunnel mouth, despairing of reaching the precious vien of water beneath him. At other times he made a kind of bucket from his helmet to use in the longed-for event of rain. But night after night the moon shone brilliantly in a cloudless sky preventing any attempt at escape. Night after night the Canadian soldier-artist waited for such a chance, only to be discouraged by the guttural sound of German voices and the silhouette of Nazi helmets against the moonlit shadows.

The ordeal was beginning to tell on the magnificent strength of spirit and body and Pepper noticed a certain light-headedness overtaking him at times. On one of these occasions, with the recklessness of desperation, he ventured some distance from his shelter. Hearing voices across the road, he called out—

"Hey! I'm a Canadian. Are you Canadian?"

The ominous silence following his outcry shocked him to better sense and he crawled rapidly back to the culvert. The brief search by Nazi soldiers led almost to the mouth of his hideout before it swerved to another area.

Pepper was forced to abandon his hopes for escape to Canadian territory, and turned his attention again to his well-digging. He dug with his small pocket knife, then with his hands and fingernails. Down, down, he burrowed, almost a foot, and still no success.

Exhausted, he fell back for one of his rest periods. He slept more fitfully now. Sometimes his rolled-up pistol and belt served as a pillow; sometimes it was his helmet. Reaching down into the hole, after one of these pauses, his fingers surely felt a bit of moisture. Greatly heartened and excited, Pepper dug deeper. At last the excavation measured in depth the length of his arm, and there his fingers actually met the cool caress of water. Eagerly the man licked his fingers, dipping into the wet clay again and again. At length, his burning fever slightly cooled, he slept again.

Waking, he looked down into his well. A good cup of clear, clean water filled the bottom of the hole. He drank slowly, and with tremendous satisfaction. Refreshed, he began to look about him with new hope.

Hungrily he watched the careless chickens, as they grubbed in the straw outside the culvert. Picking up a lassoo, which he had made from his pistol lanyard and his tie, he turned with renewed effort to his attempts to lassoo one of the chickens. These great plump red hens had been teasing him for days with their casual indifference, so close to him. Time after time he had arranged, with painstaking care, a noose in the scattered straw. Again and again he failed. Now a small, but tender-looking, pullet stepped within the fatal circle. Captain Pepper, with one unbelievably quick motion, jerked the lanyard about her leg hauling the burden swiftly into his grasp, and tightened eager fingers about the warm neck.

The unlucky fowl was too surprised to squawk. Success and his Sunday dinner had come to Captain Pepper.

Tuesday, a week and a day after his imprisonment in the tunnel, dawned not too brightly. As the morning wore into afternoon, gray clouds gathered and the skies grew overcast. Soon, it rained. The water trickled into the culvert and it became clear that by nightfall it would be too wet for shelter.

Captain Pepper looked out through the sodden straw into the drizzle.

"This has to be the time," he said to himself.

At once he began preparations for a move. He relined his helmet and again laced the camouflage netting with greenery. Finally, his preparations completed, he crawled cautiously out into the soggy ditch, on the first lap of his escape journey. This was about 4:30 in the afternoon.

As he edged his way through the wet grass, the allied field guns (twenty-five pounders) were barking across country to the left of the road. The Germans were replying with heavy shells which rumbled and crashed overhead. They appeared to explode somewhere near the crossroads where the two Captains had made their fatal turn on that Sunday which seemed so long ago. Suddenly, one of these fell short of its target. With a mighty crash, it burst in a direct hit on the house about twenty-five yards away. Captain Pepper, shaken by the explosion, watched the chimney disappear and the roof become a great gaping hole. For a few seconds, a heavy red cloud hung over the wreckage. The man in the ditch crawled back into the culvert, fearing to see Germans running to the scene of the explosion.

After waiting some time, hearing and seeing no cause for alarm, the Captain ventured out into the ditch and peered carefully over the edge. The red cloud was settling and was clearly only dust from the bricks and tiling, and not fire-smoke. Inch by inch, he made his way through the wet grass.

Soon he approached the point where he and Captain

Engler had fought it out with the Germans at cost of Engler's life. Here, with some fairly high bushes bordering the ditch on the roadside, the Captain felt safe in sitting up to look cautiously over the situation. He made sure at once that no German was in the slit-trench where he and his fellow officer had first surprised and captured the Nazi guard.

As he peered cautiously all around him, the Canadian officer made out a slight depression, like a shallow drainage channel, stretching away for some distance into the field. He saw, also, for the first time, two stone steps leading into the ditch from the road and just here a wire in the barbed fence had been cut. Reasoning that the Germans probably used these steps when going on patrol, the Captain felt uneasy and waited anxiously for signs and sounds of approaching danger. But the wet dusk seemed to hold nothing but the steady drizzle of rain, and the frequent burst of thunder from the shells and big guns. However, as this was the best point from which to survey the country around him, and so get his bearings and direction before dark, he carefully studied the ground and surroundings.

In the distance, even through the late afternoon gloom, Captain Pepper saw the church of St.. Leonard quite clearly about a mile and a half or two miles away. On a direct line with the church was a row of houses. Between him and this row stretched several rows of what appeared to be pear trees. Calculating swiftly, the Captain decided that if he could make his way through these trees, and then swing sharply to the left, he would reach the highway by which he and his comrade had left St. Leonard. There, beyond the trees, lay safety.

By 7:30 p.m. it was completely dark. The rain was still falling heavily and the man in the ditch was soaked to the skin. He felt it was time to move on. As a final precaution, he took off his wrist-watch and put it in a pocket, lest the gleam of its luminous dial should betray him to some watchful enemy. He then crawled out of the ditch and very carefully made his way through the break in the barbed-wire fence, keeping to the slight shelter of the depression that led off through the fields.

After what seemed a very long time, he came to a point opposite the first trees and crawled out of the depression to feel the ground beneath for fallen fruit. Taking time out to quench both hunger and thirst with some of the cool, juicy pears, he leaned against a tree eating as many as possible.

After that, progress was more rapid and less difficult, as he felt it was now sufficiently safe to crawl upright on hands and knees. He reached a barrier of bushes blocking the trench along which he crawled, so he climbed out into the open field and, after a few more minutes of crawling, decided it would be safe to rise to his feet. Pushing himself up accordingly, he found to his horrified surprise that he was scarcely able to stand, not to think of walking. He was unable to keep his balance and reeled drunkenly in half-circles. Lack of food and disuse of his legs for so many days had left him temporarily helpless. Persevering in his staggering efforts, however, he soon gained some control over his limbs, and stumbled through a field of cabbages. Strangely enough, this was a dangerous proceeding, because the ripe cabbage leaves broke off and cracked like pistol shots in the still night as he brushed them in passing. It was clearly necessary to skirt the cabbage patches and follow along the fences. As he continued his detouring of cabbage patches, struggling to maintain some sense of direction through increasing misery and exhaustion, Captain Pepper began to believe that most of that part of Belgium must be planted with cabbages!

For hours he wandered through a maze of rain, cabbages, distant gun-flashes, and once or twice, fleeting glimpses of stars in a clearing sky. It was then that the officer realized something had happened to his eyes, because in those glimpses, the stars blurred and re-appeared in the strangest way. The deprivation of the past days was affecting his sight. Occasionally he heard sounds which threw him to the ground in sudden alarm. Once it proved to be cows in a nearby field.

By this time he was completely lost. As he came at last in his aimless wandering to a road, he sat down beside it to try to figure out what road it might be. Sheer exhaustion overcame him and he was just dropping into an uneasy doze, when he heard sounds of a small party of men marching down the road. Instantly he flopped face down in the wet grass, covering the white of his hands. As the patrol passed him, he raised his head, peering hopefully at the shadowy outlines of the marching men.

There were four of them passing about 25 feet from the Canadian officer, and it was with a dull pang of disappointment that he noted the characteristic outlines of German helmets against the dark sky. Oddly enough, although they marched with parade precision, they did not appear to be carrying arms.

After a sufficiently safe time had elapsed, Captain Pepper ventured to crawl across the road on hands and knees. There he circled widely a mysterious house which he had noticed earlier. The rain still fell, but more fitfully, and although stars gleamed out occasionally, they failed to give any guidance to the suffering wanderer, because his treacherous eyesight refused to focus properly on the distant points of light.

Pushing his weary body to the last limit of endurance, Pepper kept on, crossing fields, struggling through ditches, avoiding trees, never sure whether or not he was heading back into enemy lines. Once or twice, he came to the same landmark, after intervals of steady moving, which proved he must be travelling in circles.

Utterly weary and numb in every sense, he alternated between moments of feeling that it all mattered very little any longer, and sudden swift fear as his mental confusion momentarily mistook a bush or tree for a human enemy.

Suddenly, out of the night, a voice challenged him. He looked up and saw four figures covering him with weapons.

He halted. Someone shouted for the password. He replied, in a weak, cracked voice, he scarcely felt to be his own.

"I don't know it."

One of the figures detached itself from the group and came towards the man swaying on the road. As the figure approached, Captain Pepper asked:

"Are you Germans?" scarcely daring to hope they were not. Until that moment, he had not realized that the conversation, carried on in his blessed Mother-tongue, meant —rescue.

It was about 3:20 in the morning of Wednesday when the Captain was picked up. After some hot stew, he was given a bed and at once slept, but not for long. At seven in the morning he was roused, and after bath, shave and breakfast, was asked to accompany officers to the top of St. Leonard's Church to point out the enemy locations he had so recently left. This enabled the artillery to correct their fire on German positions. These facts, together with maps drawn later by Captain Pepper, provided important data to Allied strategists.

So out of the ten-day ordeal of suffering and suspense, through the indomitable courage, endurance and ingenuity of a non-combatant Canadian officer, valuable information accrued to the Allied forces—not to mention the wealth of "material" the War Artist absorbed and faithfully used in his subsequent work.

INDEX

PAGE

A

Air Force Cross 9
Air Force Medal 9
Allied Pacific Fleet 110
H.M.S. Assiniboine 30-31-33

B

Ball, Rod 70-79
Brigade, Rifle, 1st Bn. 2
H.M.C.S. Battleford 30
Battle of Balaclava 4
Battle of Britain 23-27
Battle of the Scheldt 121
Bazalgette, A/Squadron Leader Ian Willoughby 6
Beardmore, F/O Eric 28
Princess Beatrix, The 12
Beatty, Admiral of the Fleet Earl 5
Bedford Basin 82
Berardi, Casa 92-97
Bernays, A/Chief Petty Officer Max 30-36
Brecht 121
Briese, F/O Carl 28
British Pacific Fleet 110
Brooke, Nursing Sister Margaret 58

C

Cesena 116
Canada Medal 10
Canadian Centennial Medal 10
2nd Canadian Division, Overseas 121
1st Canadian Parachute Battalion (See Parachute) ....
S.S. Caribou 57
Christmas, F/O Beverley E. 28
Church, T. L. (M.P. Broadview) 58-59
Cook, Lt. George 44-49
Conspicuous Gallantry Medal 36
Corbett, F/O Vaughan B. 28
Courtrai 4
Cozens, Sgt. Aubrey 6
Currie, Major David Vivian 6

D

D Company 16
Desloges, F/O Jean Paul 28
H.M.S. Dianthus 32
Dieppe 12-13-20-99-105-106

PAGE

Distinguished Conduct Medal 8
Distinguished Flying Cross 9
Distinguished Flying Medal 9
Distinguished Service Cross 7-111
Distinguished Service Medal 8
Distinguished Service Order 7
Dunn, Lt. Alexander Robert 4

E

Edwards, F/O Robert Leslie 28
Engler, Captain Joseph 121-122-124

F

Fleet Air Arm 108
Foote, Hon. Major John Weir 5-99-106
H.M.S. Formidable 108-109-110-111

G

George Cross, The 6
George Medal, The 7-47
Gorlitz 79
H.M.C.S. Grandmere 61
Grapnel Germany 29
Gray, Lt. Robert Hampton 6-107-109-110-113

H

Hoey, Capt. Charles Ferguson 5
Hurricanes 24
Hyde, F/O George G. 28

K

Kerwin, F/O John W. 28
Kiltie Regiment 51
H.M.S. King Alfred 44

L

Labatt, Lt. Col. R. H. 99-105
Le Royal 22e Regiment 91
Little, F/O Thomas B. 28
Lucas, Charles David 4

M

McGregor, F/L Gordon R. 28
McNab, Squadron Leader Ernest A. 28
Mahony, Major John Keefer 5
M.B.E. (Member of the British Empire) 90

PAGE
Merritt, Lt. Col. Charles Cecil Ingersoll 5, 12, 17, 19, 20
Military Cross 7
Military Medal 8
Molson, F/O Hartland de M. 28
C.G.S. Montcalm 81-90
Montreal Light Aeroplane Club 22, 23
Moorhouse, 2nd Lt. W. B. 4
Mount Butler 39
Mynarski, P/O Andrew Charles 6

N

Nesbitt, F/O A. Deane 28
No. 1 Fighter Squadron (R.C.A.F.) 23-27

O

Oflag VII B 106
O'Hea, Pte. Timothy 2
Okinawa 110
Onagowa Wan 111
Order of Canada, and Companions 10
Order of Canada Medal of Courage 10
Order of Canada Medal of Service 10
Order of Merit, The 11
Ortona 92
Osborn, Sgt. Major John Robert 38

P

Parachute, 1st Cdn. Bn. 65
Pepper, Capt. George 121-134
Peters, Capt. Frederick Thornton 5
Peterson, F/O Otto Jean 28
Piper, Capt. Allan 51-56
Pitcher, F/O Paul 28
Pourville 13, 20
Princess Patricia's Canadian Light Infantry 116

Q

Queen's Own Cameron Highlanders 13, 16

R

Reyno, F/O Edwin 28
Rhine River 65
Royal 22nd Regiment (See Le Royal 22e Regiment)..........
Russel, F/O Blair Dalzell 28

PAGE

S

St. John's, Newfoundland 29
St. Leonard 121-131-134
Savio, River 116
Scie, River 16
Scharnhorst 84
Seaforth Highlanders of Canada, The 115-116-120
Slocombe, Capt. Fred 80-81-82-86
S.C. (Slow Convoy) 94 29-30
Smith, Pte. Ernest Alvia 6-114-117-119-120
Smith, Major 91-92-93-94
Smither, F/O Ross 28
South Saskatchewan Regiment 13-16-19
Sprenger, F/O William B. 28
Stalag Luft III 75-78-79
Stormont, Dundas and Glengarry Highlanders 51
Suez Canal 45

T

Taverner, Capt. Benjamin 57-58
Tilston, Capt. Frederick Albert 6
Tirpitz 108-110
Topham, Cpl. Frederick George 6-63-66-68
Triquet, Capt. Paul 5-91-98

V

Victoria Cross, The 2, 5, 20, 43, 69, 98, 106, 113, 120

W

Wilkie, Nursing Sister Agnes 58
Winnipeg Grenadiers, The 39

Y

Yuile, F/O Arthur M. 28